Kristin Didn't Deserve This.

She was sunshine, laughter and warmth. She didn't belong in the cold darkness of the world he'd brought crashing into her life. *He* had put the fear in her beautiful eyes, on her lovely face, and only he could ease those fears.

But he couldn't tell her what was going on!

Then, from deep inside him, from the center of the unnamed emotion, came another voice, a quiet, gentle voice.

Tell her, it whispered. Tell her, because she was more important than orders and authorization. Tell her, because the fear she was living was cutting through him like a knife. Tell her, because she was Kristin.

"Kristin," he said, his voice slightly raspy, "look at me."

She shook her head.

"Look at me."

She slowly shifted her gaze to meet his. The knife within Josh twisted.

"My name is really Josh Quinn," he said quietly. "I'm an agent for the United States government."

Dear Reader:

Welcome! You hold in your hand a Silhouette Desire—your ticket to a whole new world of reading pleasure.

A Silhouette Desire is a sensuous, contemporary romance about passions, problems and the ultimate power of love. It is about today's woman— intelligent, successful, giving—but it is also the story of a romance between two people who are strong enough to follow their own individual paths, yet strong enough to compromise, as well.

These books are written by, for and about every woman that you are—wife, mother, sister, lover, daughter, career woman. A Silhouette Desire heroine must face the same challenges, achieve the same successes, in her story as you do in your own life.

The Silhouette reader is not afraid to enjoy herself. She knows when to take things seriously and when to indulge in a fantasy world. With six books a month, Silhouette Desire strives to meet her many moods, but each book is always a compelling love story.

For more details write to:

Jane Nicholls
Silhouette Books
PO Box 236
Thornton Road
Croydon
Surrey
CR9 3RU

ROBIN ELLIOTT
Out of the Cold

Silhouette Desire

Originally Published by Silhouette Books
a division of
Harlequin Enterprises Ltd.

First published in Great Britain in 1989 by Silhouette Books, Eton House, 18–24 Paradise Road, Richmond, Surrey TW9 1SR

© Joan Elliott Pickart 1988

Silhouette, Silhouette Desire and Colophon are Trade Marks of Harlequin Enterprises B.V.

ISBN 0 373 57478 9

22–8901

Made and printed in Great Britain

ROBIN ELLIOTT

enjoys reading, knitting, and watching football, in addition to writing romance novels. She is the mother of three daughters and devoted servant of a cocker spaniel named Cricket. Robin also writes under her own name, Joan Elliott Pickart.

Other Silhouette Books by Robin Elliott

Silhouette Desire

Call It Love
To Have It All
Picture of Love
Pennies in the Fountain
Dawn's Gift
Brooke's Chance
Betting Man
Silver Sands
Lost and Found

For DEO

Prologue

Joshua Quinn strode down the hall, then stopped outside a closed door. He glanced around, hearing nothing and seeing only the eerie glow of the amber lights left on in the building during the night.

Tucking a plain white folder under his arm, he reached into his pocket for a pack of cigarettes. He shook one loose and lighted it with a thin gold lighter, then inhaled deeply as he returned the cigarettes and lighter to his pocket.

As he squinted against the rising smoke, he forced himself to gain control of his raging anger and frustration. He was dressed, he realized, entirely in black, and while he hadn't chosen it consciously, the color definitely reflected his mood.

With more force than necessary he jammed the cigarette into the sand-filled receptacle by the door, then

entered the room. The two men sitting at the table got
to their feet immediately, but Josh waved them back
into their seats. He dropped the folder onto the table,
pulled out a chair, propped his foot on it and crossed
his arms on his knee. He looked directly at the men,
who shifted uncomfortably in their chairs. The tension in the small, sparsely furnished room was nearly
palpable.

"I read the report," Josh said quietly. "Now I want
to hear it from you two. It took eighteen months for
us to put this together, and it was blown in the last
step." He paused. "Why?"

"Damn it, Quinn," one of the men said. "It's all in
the report. Henri Duquesne died. The rendezvous was
set. Every detail had been checked and double-
checked. The plan was perfect, with no chance of any
slipups—and then the old guy croaked."

"He had a deteriorating heart condition," Josh
said. "Why didn't we know that?"

"He didn't tell anyone," the man said, throwing up
his hands. "Government secrets should be kept so
well. His housekeeper was the only one who knew."

"According to the report," Josh said, glancing at
the folder, "Henri had her mail a small package from
Paris the day before he died. We've got the housekeeper in a safehouse, at least. All she remembers
about the package is that she mailed it to the United
States, to Maine. She was too worried about Henri's
health to pay any closer attention to it."

Josh shook his head, then straightened, shoving his
hands into his back pockets. He walked slowly to the
door, retraced his steps, then repeated his trek before
returning to stand by the edge of the table.

Seconds ticked into minutes.

No one spoke.

"All Henri's contacts were in Paris," Josh finally said. "Apparently he knew he didn't have time to get the word out that he was in trouble, then wait for one of you to get to him. So he took a desperate and foolish step. He had it mailed."

"That's the way we figure it," the other man said. "We need to check his computer file to see who might have been his connections in the States."

"I did that before I came in here," Josh said, flipping the file open.

"And?"

"There's only one candidate. I'm catching a plane out in an hour to go to the good old U.S. of A. Temple, Maine, to be exact."

"Temple, Maine?"

Josh looked at the open file. "It's thirty miles in from the coast, population ten thousand. The nearest big city is forty miles away. There's no major industry in Temple, so people either own or work in small shops or commute to the city."

"Sounds like a real exciting place," one of the men said dryly. "So? Who's in swinging Temple, Maine?"

"The only person we have a record of Henri knowing in the States," Josh said. "His niece, Kristin Duquesne."

One

────

Kristin Duquesne lowered the bamboo shades on the last window of the gallery. She smiled indulgently at her own sense of gloominess, knowing she'd registered the same emotion each autumn for the past five years when it had been time to take her two-month vacation.

She also knew that within hours she would be filled with anticipation of the freedom the months ahead would bring, as she would be able to paint whenever and wherever she pleased. She would be able to unwind from the hectic pace of meeting with the countless artists who supplied the wide variety of works she offered in her gallery. All the items she'd ordered would be delivered in time for the busy Christmas season, and by then Kristin would have enjoyed weeks of painting and be ready to face the holiday rush with enthusiasm.

Her life, Kristin had told herself more than once, was close to perfect. The past five years had brought her much happiness, good friends and financial security, and she was extremely grateful.

But there was one niggling flutter in her heart whose identity was no secret to her. She had always seen herself as half of a loving relationship and as the mother of children. She'd thought she'd found her special man once, but she'd been wrong, very wrong. And so her life was almost, but not quite, perfect.

"Kristin?"

She turned to her assistant, an attractive woman in her fifties. "You caught me, Martha," Kristin said, smiling. "I was doing my usual pouting routine because for the next two months I won't be coming here every day. Then, the minute I get home, I'll feel like a kid out of school for the summer."

Martha laughed. "I understand. It's like years ago, when I thought I'd go out of my mind if I didn't get out of the house for a while and have a breather from my three babies. But the minute the baby-sitter showed up I would start to think of a hundred reasons why I shouldn't leave them. I, my dear, will take very good care of your baby—the gallery—as I always do."

Kristin crossed the room and gave Martha a warm hug. "I know you will, and I thank you. Remember, you can always call me if—"

"Yes, Mother," Martha said with a chuckle, "I know."

"I give up," Kristin said, laughing. "I'm on my way out the door. You're leaving now, aren't you?"

"In a few minutes. I'm waiting for a call from the outfit where we get our stationery. You go on. I'll lock up."

"I'll talk to you soon, Martha," Kristin said, slipping on her red parka.

"Not *too* soon," Martha called after her as Kristin went out the front door.

Outside, Kristin stopped and turned, her gaze sweeping over the gallery. How proud her parents would be, she thought. This had been her dream since she'd been a child, and they'd encouraged her. She knew they would have approved of what she had done with the money left to her on their sudden and tragic deaths.

It had been over a year before she could bear to acknowledge that the money was even there, waiting for her, but at last she had emerged from her cocoon of grief. Grief that had come so soon after she'd had her heart shattered by loving and trusting the wrong man. How unhappy she had been back then, how sure she would never smile again.

Now, she knew, her smiles were genuine, and the peacefulness within her was like a precious gift to be cherished.

She nodded in satisfaction as she looked at the gallery, realizing that her gloomy mood had already faded into oblivion. She had a quart of Mattie Olson's clam chowder waiting for her at home, as well as a thick new novel she was eager to read, and the wood in the hearth was ready for a match to be set to it to bring it to a warming, welcoming blaze. Fantastic.

With a smile that she made no attempt to hide, Kristin set off down the sidewalk, her destination the lot a block away where she had parked her car.

Josh cupped his hands around the flame of the gold lighter and lighted a cigarette, inhaling deeply as he watched Kristin Duquesne walk away from the gallery.

She was prettier than her photo, he decided. There was a lovely translucent quality to her skin that hadn't come across in the grainy print. Her blond hair fell in soft waves to her shoulders, and she didn't appear to mind that the chill wind was whipping it into tumbled disarray. Although he couldn't see her eyes clearly from his shadowed place across the street, he knew they were blue. She had delicate features, was five foot six and was slender but not skinny.

Oh, yeah, Josh thought, he knew a lot about Kristin Duquesne, including the fact that she'd lost her parents six years ago. The year before her parents' death, she'd been engaged, but she'd returned the ring to the guy a month before the wedding had been scheduled to take place.

And he knew that Kristin was about to start her annual two-month vacation, during which she would paint, travel, see a small circle of friends. There was no lover.

Joshua Quinn also knew that from the moment that Henri Duquesne's housekeeper had mailed that package, Kristin Duquesne's life had been in danger.

Henri had panicked, Josh thought, shaking his head. But then, dying men often did.

He crushed the cigarette beneath his shoe and stepped from between the buildings, immediately hunching his shoulders against the cold. He wore a heavy sheepskin jacket over a sweater, but the wind seemed to slice right through him. Damn cold.

He strolled along the sidewalk, resisting the urge to quicken his step to escape the biting wind. He wanted to give Kristin ample time to reach her car and drive away—straight home, he hoped. It had taken several days to put the wheels in motion that would afford him the means to be close to Kristin, and he had no more time to waste. The package was on its way to her.

Josh had spent two hours that afternoon carefully scrutinizing Kristin's neighborhood. Her house was a medium-size one-story structure on a large lot. The street was short and contained only three houses on either side, and a wooded area stood at the end of the paved road. Two of the houses across the street from Kristin were empty and for sale. The woods, the vacant homes and the fact that Kristin's house was next to the woods did nothing for Josh's peace of mind, and he was frowning as he drove toward her neighborhood.

Darkness was falling quickly—and with it the temperature—as Josh pulled into the driveway of the house next door to Kristin's. He saw her car in her driveway, and lights were glowing behind the drawn curtains on the windows.

He got out of his car and crossed the lawn to Kristin's house, then walked up the three steps to the wooden porch. The screen was slightly ajar, he noted, and there was no window or peephole in the wooden door behind it. He was about to find out if Miss Duquesne was the cautious type or just threw open the door to welcome whoever was standing there. Whether or not *he* would be welcome to come inside would depend on how well he pushed his ever-so-charming button.

He pulled open the screen and knocked on the solid door beyond it.

Okay, Kristin, he mentally directed, ask who it is before you open it.

The door opened.

Damn, Josh thought. Then he smiled and said, "Hello. I'm sorry if I disturbed you." Much, *much* prettier than her picture.

Kristin opened her mouth to speak, then closed it when she realized that absolutely no sound was going to come out. She hadn't really known who might be knocking on her door, and the imposing figure of the man standing before her had caught her off guard.

Goodness, she thought, he was gorgeous. Tall, broad shouldered, tanned. His hair was dark and thick, and he had a straight nose and high cheekbones. And those eyes—so dark, so piercing. And there was something else, as well: a strange energy, an aura of power, seemed to emanate from this man.

She cleared her throat. "Yes?" she said politely.

"Do you always open the door without knowing who's on the other side?" That, Josh thought, was *not* charming.

"I don't believe," Kristin said tightly, "that it's any of your business."

"You're right. I'm sorry," he said, switching from his sixty-watt to his hundred-watt smile. "I've got a problem, but that's no excuse for my taking it out on you."

"Problem?"

"I'm staying at the house next door, and the utilities were supposed to be on, but they're not. I was wondering if I could use your phone to see if I can get someone out here."

"You're staying at Dr. Jameson's house? They only decided a few days ago to go on vacation to Hawaii. They said it had been years since they'd done anything on impulse, and they were so excited about the trip. They didn't mention anyone staying at the house while they were gone, though."

Ah, Josh thought, so Miss Duquesne was a bit cautious after all. From one of his men he'd gotten a quick phone report regarding the Jamesons that had included some little tidbits obtained from a jangled Carol Jameson. He'd have to play this exactly right.

"Well, as you know," he said, "the Jamesons decided at the last minute to go on this trip. They felt it was a perk of Dr. Jameson finally retiring. I happened to be visiting their son, Jeff, when they called him to say they were going. One thing led to another, and here I am."

"You're a friend of Jeff's?"

"We go way back. I've been telling him for years that he has an unfair advantage with his two different-colored eyes. That fascinates the women he meets."

"I see," Kristin said slowly, a slight frown on her face.

Well, damn, Josh thought, wasn't that enough for her? He was freezing his tush off while Kristin decided if he was on the level. Okay, what else? There was a black-and-white stray cat....

"By the way," he said, "Mrs. Jameson said to tell you to watch for the magic lady, whatever that means."

Kristin laughed. "Well, that erases any doubt in my mind as to whether you actually know Carol." She stepped back. "Please come in, Mr.—"

"Quinn. Josh Quinn," he said, coming into the room. Her laughter was nice, he thought, and she had one of those light-up-the-face smiles. "Call me either Josh or Quinn. It runs about fifty-fifty with the people I know. Is there really a magic lady around here?"

"Indeed, there is...Josh. Magic Lady is a stray cat who spends her time between here and the Jamesons'. She has the most uncanny ability to get into our houses when we're not looking—hence the name Carol and I gave her. We both feed her and spoil her rotten. It's been over a week since I've seen her, though. I hope nothing has happened to her."

"I'm sure she'll show up." He paused. "Mrs. Jameson told me that you're Kristin Duquesne, that you own a gallery here in Temple and that you're a talented painter yourself." He glanced around the room. "This is nice, homey—" his gaze lingered on the fire crackling on the hearth "—and warm. My place is freezing."

"Oh, goodness, your utilities," Kristin said. "And here I stand talking about a silly cat. Take off your coat. The phone and book are over on that desk. Help yourself. I've got something on the stove, if you'll excuse me."

"Sure, and thank you, Kristin."

It was only her name, she told herself. Then why did it sound so...so sensuous when Josh said it? She spun around and went into the kitchen.

Josh watched her go, then took off his coat and draped it over the back of a chair. While he would have preferred to stand in front of the fire to remove the last of the chill from his body, he instead crossed the room to the desk on the far wall. He flipped through the phone book for effect, dialed a number, then carried on a mumbled conversation with a recorded message that kept repeating the time and temperature.

"Well, okay," he finally said in a clear voice, "if that's the best you can do, I'll just have to live with it. Bye." He replaced the receiver, went to the kitchen and leaned against the doorjamb.

"Trouble?" Kristin said, glancing up at him from where she stood at the stove. Saints above, he was dressed all in black. The sweater stretched across broad shoulders, a muscled chest, a flat stomach and— Enough, she chided herself. She'd seen handsome, well-built men before. But still...

"Someone messed up the service order," Josh said. "My utilities are scheduled to be turned on tomorrow. They can't do it tonight. I sure wish the Jamesons hadn't decided to turn everything off while they were away. Well, no matter, I'll stay at a motel." Nope, he thought. There was only Betty's Bed and Breakfast, and it was closed up tight. Your ball, Kristin Duquesne.

"There's nowhere to stay," she said, frowning. "Betty's Bed and Breakfast is closed. She left last week to visit her daughter. The closest motel is forty miles away.''

"Forget that. I'm bushed. Well, I'll just wrap up in a bunch of blankets tonight. It won't kill me." The hell it wouldn't.

"Well, I . . . Look, first things first. Would you like a bowl of clam chowder?''

"Is that what smells so terrific?" Josh said, smiling. "You do understand that I should politely refuse, because I've already bothered you by asking to use your phone. However . . ." His smile grew bigger.

"However?" she said, matching his expression.

"I'm starving, the chowder smells great, and I'll set the table, do the dishes—you name it—if you'll give me a bowl of it."

She laughed. "At least you're honest."

Right, he thought dryly. "Can I wash my hands, Kristin?''

"Help yourself," she said, reaching in the cupboard for two bowls. "The bathroom is down the hall." And if he didn't quit saying her name like that, he'd be able to help himself to *her* when she fell into a dead faint at his feet. At least she was doing a super job of avoiding looking at him for too long at a time. She had a sneaking suspicion that gazing into his eyes for more than a fleeting moment could be dangerous.

Josh washed and dried his hands, then left the water running. The bathroom, he soon discovered, connected the two bedrooms. Kristin had left a lamp burning on the nightstand next to her bed, and Josh swept his gaze over the room, registering the location of the window and the fact that there was another phone.

He moved through the bathroom into the dark room beyond. Both bedrooms were also accessible from the hallway. He closed the door, turned on the light and quickly scanned the area. Kristin's studio, he realized. The was an easel by the window, and the faint odor of oil paint hung in the air.

Josh switched off the light and opened the door, then returned to the bathroom to shut off the water. He reentered the kitchen just as Kristin placed a bowl of tossed salad on the table.

"Coffee?" she asked, glancing at him.

"Only if you're having some."

"It's ready. Please, sit down, Josh."

"I'd like to help."

"There's nothing to do. It's a very simple meal." So, she hadn't imagined it earlier, Kristin mused. As soon as Josh had come back into the kitchen, the room had seemed smaller. It wasn't just his size. There was something about him that seemed to overwhelm the area around him. Heaven knew he was overwhelming *her*. She was rattled—and thoroughly disgusted with herself.

Josh sat down at the table, watching as Kristin reached for coffee mugs. She was nervous, he could tell. He'd really have to watch his step. Damn, she was so feminine, so delicate. But he would be gentle with her when he made love to her and— What the hell! he fumed. Where was his mind headed? Yes, he had to stay close to her, get her to trust him and get used to having him around until he could get his hands on that package. But make love to her? No way.

"Josh?"

He looked up quickly, surprised to see that Kristin was sitting across the table from him. Wonderful. If she were an enemy there'd be a knife in his throat.

"Sorry," he said, smiling.

"Dig in while it's hot. This is homemade chowder. My friend Mattie Olson made it."

Josh shoveled in a spoonful. He hated clam chowder. "It's delicious."

They ate in silence for several minutes.

"What made you decide to come here?" Kristin finally asked pleasantly. "Temple isn't exactly a bustling tourist attraction."

"I don't like crowds. I just want to relax, unwind."

"You have a high-pressure job?"

That was putting it mildly. "I'm a troubleshooter for a computer firm. I'm sent in whenever the machines go down. I have to analyze the situation and fix it as quickly as possible so that the company isn't way off schedule. It gets stressful."

"I can imagine. You must travel a great deal, too."

"Yeah," he said.

"Do you have family?" A wife. Why hadn't she thought of that before? But wouldn't he have brought her on a vacation with him?

"No. No family."

No wife, Kristin thought. And she was registering such a rush of relief that she couldn't believe it. "I don't have any family, either."

"Really?" he said. "And here I thought with a name like Duquesne you'd be related to the royalty of France, or whatever it is they have over there."

She smiled. "Nope. I had an uncle that lived in Paris, but he was killed in World War II, so I never even met him."

Interesting, Josh mused. It made sense, though. Henri had been a wild kid, no doubt the black sheep of the family, and had been disowned years ago.

"I'm expecting some important papers," he said, "but I didn't see a mailbox in front of the Jamesons'."

"They're lined up at the end of the street," Kristin said. "The mail is delivered in the early afternoon."

"Okay," he said, nodding. Excellent. All he had to do was intercept the mailman and offer to take Kristin's mail to her. Even *Josh* didn't have the authority to take the mail out of her box. The timing would have to be just right.

"There's a little more chowder," Kristin said.

"No," Josh replied quickly. "No, thank you."

"How about a piece of chocolate cake?"

"Now you're singing my tune." He grinned at her.

"I'll get it," she said, rising.

Josh again watched her move across the room, and he felt the heat shoot through the lower regions of his body. Damn. This wasn't like him at all. His mind and body were fine-tuned, under his command, and that included his libido! He had no idea why Kristin was getting to him like this, but it was going to stop.

When Kristin returned to the table, she moved to hand Josh his dessert just as he reached for it. His fingers curled around hers at the edge of the plate, and in the same instant he met her gaze.

Neither moved. Or spoke.

Incredible heat wove up and through and around them, creating currents of sexuality that were nearly palpable.

A rushing noise echoed in Kristin's ears.

Damn it, Quinn, snap out of it, Josh ordered himself.

Dear heaven, Kristin thought frantically, what was this man doing to her?

Pulling his gaze from Kristin's, Josh took the plate from her and plunked it in front of him.

"Well," he said. Oh, brilliant, he chided himself. She looked scared to death. But she wasn't the only one who was shaken up. "This cake looks...great." Ah, hell!

Kristin swallowed and attempted a smile that failed. "I hope you like it," she managed to say. What had happened? Their fingers had touched; that was all. She had to put distance between her and Josh Quinn now, right now.

"Kristin, don't," he said, his voice low and husky.

"What?"

"Don't run. I'm not going to hurt you."

She lifted her chin. "I'm not frightened of you, Josh."

"Then why do you suddenly look as though you think I'm going to ravish your body in the kitchen sink?"

"Oh, for heaven's sake," she said with a wobbly laugh.

He smiled at her. "I'm just going to sit here and eat my cake. Okay?"

"Yes, okay," she said, drawing a steadying breath. "Josh..." She paused. "Josh, I'm acting very foolish, and I realize it, but I'm not in the habit of inviting strangers into my home and offering them dinner."

"We both know the Jamesons," he said, leaning toward her slightly. "That has to be worth something."

"Well, yes, but— Oh, never mind."

"You know, when you opened the door without asking who was there I thought you were sort of careless. I was wrong. You're extremely cautious. In fact, I get the feeling that you don't trust very easily at all."

"No," she said softly, "I guess I don't."

Uh-oh, Josh thought. Not good. She might very well tell him to take a hike, and he had to stay close to her until he had that package, because he sure as hell wasn't the only one after it.

"I said I wouldn't hurt you, Kristin. I'm asking you to trust me on that."

He took a bite of the cake. He supposed it was good, but at the moment it tasted like sawdust.

Trust him? Kristin's mind echoed. She hadn't really trusted any man since—

"Great cake," Josh said. He gave her a slow, lazy smile as he folded his arms over his chest and rocked back on two legs of the chair. "Now, I ask you, how can you not trust a guy who is crazy about chocolate cake?" He paused. "We're going to be neighbors of sorts for a while. Where's the harm in spending a little time together...as friends?" He swept his hand across the left side of his chest.

"You're making me feel very childish, Josh," she said quietly. "I don't usually overreact this way." She got up from the table, went to a cupboard and returned with an ashtray, which she set in front of him.

Josh thudded the chair back onto all four legs. "How did you know I smoke?"

"My father smoked. Every night after dinner he'd reach in his shirt pocket for his cigarettes. I saw you move your hand across your chest, looking for your cigarettes." She picked up the bowls and carried them to the sink.

Kristin Duquesne was observant, intelligent, Josh thought. She was also skittish, wary of him. He definitely had his work cut out for him here.

"So, how about it?" he said as she returned to the table. He got to his feet and picked up the two mugs. "Are we going to be friends?"

Kristin looked at him for a long moment. "We'll see."

Two

Josh took a final drag off the cigarette, then flicked it into the fire as he stood by the hearth, staring down into the leaping orange flames. He absently tapped the gold lighter on the mantel as a frown knit his dark brows. He'd left the kitchen as Kristin had been doing the final wiping-up of the counters and table. He hoped it would give her a chance to calm down.

And him a chance to berate himself for his asinine behavior.

He was thirty-eight years old, he fumed, not some teenager. He was also highly trained, in the methods necessary to guarantee that he had an edge, the ability to keep himself alive, one step ahead of those attempting to kill him. He had total control of body, mind, emotions. Nothing and no one got past the walls he'd constructed around every facet of his being.

Yet, he knew, he was slightly off the mark when it came to Kristin Duquesne. He wasn't as alert, and his reflexes weren't quite as sharp, when he fell under the spell she seemed capable of casting over him. And she wasn't even trying!

It had happened twice. Once when he'd looked up to find that she'd already joined him at the table, and then when their hands had touched when she'd handed him the cake, he'd been pulled off course by a woman. Well, he was back in control now, and he intended to stay there.

"That's an interesting lighter."

Josh spun around to find Kristin standing next to him. Damn it to hell! She'd done it again. She'd sneaked up on him, and it would serve him right if he were lying on the floor in a pool of his own blood.

Easy, Quinn, he told himself. He couldn't take it out on her, or she'd show him the door. But what in blazes was this woman doing to him?

"I've had this lighter for many, many years," he said turning to face the fire again.

"I can see that," she said, smiling. "You've worn the gold away where you hold it. Would you care for a brandy?"

Josh slipped the lighter into his pocket. "If you're having one."

Kristin went back into the kitchen. A few minutes later she returned and handed Josh a brandy snifter and settled on the sofa, which faced the fireplace. Josh rested his arm on the mantel and took a sip. He shifted slightly to look at her.

"You're extremely observant," he said. "You catch details that most people would never notice."

Kristin laughed softly. "I know. It's the artist in me. Ever since I was young I've subconsciously looked further than what I was seeing on the surface. I drove my parents crazy at times. Whenever my mother was upset she wore a special apron. She wasn't even aware of it. Something would distress her and she'd put on that apron to make dinner. There were few secrets kept from me."

Which meant, Josh thought dryly, that he'd better stay on his toes a lot better than he had so far.

"But then..." Kristin began.

"Then?" Josh prompted her.

"I don't know," she said, staring into her brandy. "I think I came to believe that because of my ability to see beneath the surface I was immune to any kind of deception. I discovered that wasn't true. I've lost faith in my own judgment in some areas."

Such as men, Josh thought. "Such as?"

Kristin looked up at him. "Oh, it isn't important. I was just chatting."

"It's men, isn't it?" Josh said. "That's why you've seemed scared of me at times. You invited me into your home, then you've registered flashes of fear that maybe you shouldn't have done it."

He swirled the liquor in the glass and watched the glow of the flames from the fire color the brandy varying hues. He looked at Kristin again.

"You could say this is none of my business," he said, "but I think it is, due to the fact that I'm standing here in your living room. I'd guess you've been hurt in the past by a man, Kristin, and you've decided it's safer not to trust any man than to run the risk of being hurt again."

"You're right," she said, setting her snifter on an end table. "It's none of your business."

"Isn't it?" he said in a low voice, watching her.

She snapped her head around to meet his gaze, anger flashing in her blue eyes. "No."

"Wrong," he said, placing his drink on the mantel. "I'm paying the price for something someone else did. I said I wouldn't hurt you, I asked you to trust me about that, but you're weighing my words and actions against what some other man did to you. I'm fighting a ghost."

"Josh, I—"

"I can't fight what I can't see. It's up to you to decide if you're going to trust me. It's important to me, Kristin." Only because of the assignment, of course, he told himself. "Will you trust me? Will you give us a chance to have a foundation of trust for our...friendship?"

No! Kristin's mind screamed. She couldn't trust Josh Quinn, because there was something strange happening between them, something unsettling and frightening. She'd felt it when they'd touched. She wanted to trust him. She really did. It had been so very long—and she'd been so very lonely—since she'd trusted.

"Kristin?"

"I want to trust you, Josh," she said in a voice that was hardly more than a whisper. "I want to, but—"

"That's all it takes," he interrupted. "Your wanting to. Because I'm not going to give you any cause not to trust me." Fantastic, his mind hummed. He was chipping away at the wall she'd built, and she was going to give him a chance. Man, he'd like to get his hands on that sleazeball she'd been engaged to. Well, Josh Quinn was in Kristin's life now, and he was going to...

Josh reached for the snifter and took a deep swallow of brandy, which burned his throat. Going to do what? Concentrate on getting the package, damn it. The feeling of relief he'd gotten when Kristin had said she wanted to trust him had nothing to do with the assignment, and he knew it. He'd reacted to her words as a man, pure and simple. Damn. He was losing it again.

"Josh?" Kristin said. "What's wrong? You suddenly look very angry."

"What? Oh, no, I'm not angry. Nothing's wrong. I just have a lot on my mind. That's why I need this vacation. I've really been pushing myself at work lately."

"I'm on vacation as of today, too."

"Oh?"

"The last few months have been hectic. I've had to meet with all the artists I deal with to place my orders for Christmas. The pace is exhausting. Now I have time to relax, paint to my heart's content, and I'll be ready for the holiday rush. Steady traffic comes through Temple, even though the town is isolated to an extent. For the next two months my assistant will run the gallery."

"Sounds good," Josh said, nodding. He chuckled. "Not only that, but you're starting your vacation in a nice, warm house—complete with all the utilities turned on. I can't believe they messed up a simple service order like that. I guess you don't appreciate heat, lights and hot water until you don't have them."

Thunder rumbled outside, and Kristin and Josh glanced up at the ceiling, then at each other.

"Oh, dear," Kristin said, "it's going to rain."

Thank goodness, Josh thought. He needed all the help he could get. "Yep."

He'd simply have to stay there tonight, Kristin reasoned with herself. With the coming rain, his place would be that much damper and colder. All he'd get out of his vacation would be a case of pneumonia. So she'd let him sleep on her sofa, there in front of the fire. It was the only humane thing to do.

Josh, spending the night in her house? Oh, mercy. Now, stop it, she chided herself. She'd said she wanted to trust Josh, and she'd meant it. She *did* trust him. There, she'd said it—at least to herself. Next step? Tell him that the only sensible solution to his dilemma was to spend the night on her sofa. Fine.

"Josh, I..." She paused. "...I think you should spend the night with me." Oh, no! She rushed on. "What I mean is, you could sleep here, on the sofa. That thunder is getting closer, and it's definitely going to rain, and your place is going to be cold...." Was she babbling? she asked herself. "What do you think?"

She was babbling, Josh decided, making sure he didn't smile. She was really shaking herself up with her suggestion that he spend the night. But he had to stay in order to accomplish what he needed to do.

"Well," he said slowly, as though thinking it over, "I certainly wouldn't want to be the cause of any gossip about you."

She shrugged. "No one will know. That's not to say people don't like gossip around here, but it's not as if we're going to hang a sign on the porch advertising the fact that you slept here." She paused. "Your car isn't in my driveway, is it?"

"No, I walked over." Rain was beginning to beat heavily on the roof. Josh chuckled. "That rain even sounds cold. All right, Kristin, I'll accept your most gracious offer. I'd really appreciate the use of your sofa tonight. Now, tell me about your oil painting." Damn, she'd never said she painted with oils. She'd only said she painted. "Or do you use oils? We laymen just naturally assume that."

"I do," she said, smiling, "and I don't limit my subjects to just landscapes or portraits. I do a little bit of everything. I sketch first in pencil and go from there. I show some of my own work at the gallery, and it sells very well, much to my delight."

"It must be quite a feeling to see something come alive under your hand. I don't have talent in any of the arts." The talents he had would scare her out of her socks. Kill before you're killed. Now, there was a charming after-dinner conversation topic.

For the next hour Josh steered the subject matter toward things he knew interested her and would keep her talking. The rain continued to fall, but he kept part of his mind tuned for any outside noise not connected with the storm. He commented on things Kristin said, urged her to continue; part of him, though, was outside, listening, staying alert. But there was nothing, only the rain.

"The fire is dying down," Kristin said, rising.

"Tell me where the logs are," Josh said.

"There are dry ones in the laundry room off the kitchen. You haven't moved from in front of those flames. You must be cooked."

"No, it feels great. I'll get some logs."

Kristin watched Josh disappear into the kitchen. He seemed to have a real aversion to the cold. He'd certainly picked the wrong place for his vacation, then. It wasn't too bright for a person to come to Maine this time of year if he detested the cold. Well, it was none of her business, and he *was* there. Brother, was he ever there!

Josh returned, carrying an armload of logs with ease, then set them on the hearth. He hunkered down and placed a large log on the flames, then reached for the poker.

Kristin stared at the wide expanse of his shoulders, at the fascinating way the muscles in his back bunched and moved beneath his sweater. And seeing the tight contours of his buttocks. She was gawking! she admonished herself.

She cleared her throat, ignoring the funny flutter in the pit of her stomach, and examined her fingernails.

Josh pushed himself to his feet, then sat on the sofa—a full cushion away from Kristin. He stretched his long legs out in front of him and crossed them at the ankles, then laced his fingers over his flat stomach, staring into the flames.

Kristin stole a glance at him from under her lashes. Not fair, she decided. Now it was thighs...muscled thighs beneath tight pants. And his hands, with those long fingers, callused, gentle fingers. Fingers that had been so warm when they'd touched hers.

"I'm really beginning to realize," Josh said, his voice low, "how badly I needed this vacation. I can feel myself relaxing more each minute." Wrong. He was wired. He was also, damn it, very aware of the woman a few feet away from him on that sofa.

"Good," Kristin replied. "That's exactly what vacations are for. Actually, though, I can't imagine why you came here. You seem to hate the cold."

A stark picture flashed before Josh's eyes. It was a scene he'd thought he'd long forgotten. He saw himself as a little boy, huddled under a threadbare blanket on a bare mattress. And shivering with cold . . . so cold.

Josh shifted upward, chasing the memory from his mind, angry that it had come back to him after so many years. Leaning forward, he rested his elbows on his knees and made a steeple of his fingers.

"Yeah, I do hate the cold," he said quietly.

"Where did you grow up?"

Here, there, everywhere, he thought. On the streets. In empty buildings. In alleys. "Chicago."

"I imagine it gets very cold and damp there in the winter."

"Very," Josh said, nodding. "As for coming here for a vacation, I really didn't think it through. I finished a job, knew I was more than just physically tired, then happened to run into Jeff Jameson. We were sitting around his place, getting caught up on each other's news, when his folks called to say they were going to Hawaii. Jeff suggested I use their house to unwind, the Jamesons agreed, and here I am." He looked up at the ceiling as the rain continued to beat against the roof. "I must be out of my mind."

Kristin laughed. "There will be some lovely days. You'll see. How long are you planning to stay?"

"I'm not sure."

Kristin waited, expecting Josh to elaborate on his answer, to say it depended on the weather or his job or how long it took him to get bored. There was a restless energy emanating from him, as though he was having a difficult time sitting still, despite his claim that he was relaxing more as time passed. There was an air about him of leashed power just waiting to break loose. How dramatic she was being. Apparently he wasn't going to say any more on the subject of the length of his stay. He'd slouched back into his previous position. Back to thighs, muscled thighs, and those hands, and—Kristin, stop it!

A silence fell. It was a silence that should have been uncomfortable, since the two people in the room were virtual strangers, but it wasn't strained; it was simply, peacefully quiet. Private thoughts were accompanied by the drumming of the rain and the crackling of the fire.

Then the atmosphere slowly shifted, drifted, changed. The man became even more acutely aware of the woman, as the woman did the man. As if pulled by invisible threads at exactly the same moment, they turned their heads.

Blue eyes and eyes of ebony met and held.

Kristin felt suddenly strange, light-headed, as though she had to remember to breathe.

Josh felt the heat shoot through the lower regions of his body.

The invisible threads tugged once more.

The man and the woman moved.

Just enough . . . just close enough.

Josh slipped his hand to the nape of Kristin's neck and murmured her name in a dark, rumbly voice, causing a shiver to course through her.

He lowered his head toward hers...slowly... closer...closer...

The invisible threads spun their web.

And he kissed her.

Softly, sensuously, parting her lips, meeting her tongue, he kissed her.

The purr from Kristin's throat was matched by the groan that came from deep within Josh's chest. He slid his arm around her waist as she lifted her hands to his neck, inching her fingers into his thick hair. He pulled her to him, crushing her breasts to his chest as the kiss intensified, became urgent, frenzied, hungry.

Josh drank of Kristin's sweetness, inhaled her aroma, felt the lush fullness of her breasts against the hard wall of his chest. Heat coiled within him. He filled his senses with all that she was and wanted more. Much more.

He wanted Kristin Duquesne as he had no woman before.

Kristin couldn't think; she could only feel—feel and taste and savor Josh Quinn. She was awash with desire, the rhythmic motion of Josh's tongue against and around hers matching the pulsing tempo deep inside her in a dark, secret place that ached with a sweet pain. Her breasts grew heavy, wanting, needing to be caressed by Josh's strong hands. His mouth on hers was ecstasy, evoking passion within her like none she had ever known before.

Raging need and burning desire within Josh tumbled together with an emotion he didn't know, couldn't name. It was all a churning maze of confusion, of knowing in the passion-laden recesses of his mind that for the first time in his adult life, he was losing control of himself. He was caught in a web, a silken web, but the bonds were strong, holding him, urging him to stay there in the haven of Kristin's arms.

No! his reason insisted.

It was warm there, another inner voice whispered to him. So warm. Staying with Kristin meant he would never be cold again. She had the ability to warm his body and, dear God, his heart. He wanted to stay.

The assignment, reason taunted him. The package—his purpose for being there. The sweet warmth of Kristin Duquesne was dangerous.

A shudder ripped through Josh, a pain as real as a knife slicing through his gut. He pushed aside the unnamed emotion, buried it in a dusty, forgotten corner of his mind. Quieting the whispering, gentle voice within him that he'd never heard before, he paid heed to the screaming messages in his mind.

He lifted his head and moved back.

Away from the warmth of Kristin.

She slowly raised her lashes to gaze up at him, and his heart thundered. He saw the desire in the smoky blue of her eyes, saw her moist, kiss-swollen lips, saw the flush of passion on her cheeks. He wanted to move into her embrace again. Hold her. Touch her. Kiss her. Feel her respond once more in total abandon to his lips and tongue.

He wanted Kristin's warmth.

"Josh?" she said in a mere whisper.

"I'm sorry," he said, his voice husky. No, he wasn't sorry. He didn't want to stop kissing her, not ever. "I shouldn't have done that.'' What was that strange feeling, damn it? he wondered.

"*We* did it," she said, then drew a steadying breath. "I wanted you to kiss me, Josh. It wasn't the most ladylike performance of my life, but facts are facts." She shook her head. "What are you doing to me? I've never behaved like this before. I'm the one who's sorry, if I've led you to believe I'm a different kind of woman than I am."

"You didn't lead me on, Kristin. You're not a tease."

"This is frightening, Josh. I don't know what happened. I wanted you to kiss me, I wanted you to... Oh, my God, I can't believe this."

"Shhh, it's all right. Come here," he said, drawing her into the circle of his arms. He felt her stiffen. "I'm just going to hold you, show you that you're safe with me."

She nestled against him, resting her head on his shoulder. "But," she said, managing a bit of a laugh, "are you safe from me?"

He chuckled, and Kristin could feel the sound ripple through his body. She was aware of the steely muscles beneath his sweater, the power in his massive frame. But his kiss and his hands had been so gentle, she mused dreamily. Never had she responded to a man as she had to Josh. And sitting close to him now in front of the fire felt so right, so good.

And, yes, frightening at the same time.

Kristin gave a sigh born of confusion and doubt and weariness, and Josh's hold on her tightened.

He focused his mind on why he was really there, and he clenched his teeth. Nothing and no one, he vowed fiercely, was going to harm this woman. He would keep her safe, protect her from those who would have no qualms about hurting her to get their hands on the package.

Kristin felt Josh tense, felt the coiled readiness of his muscles. She glanced up at him and saw the hard set of his jaw, the coldness in his eyes as he stared into the flames dancing in the fireplace.

Oh, he was complicated, this man, she thought. He was there, holding her, yet now he wasn't really there. His mind and his body were concentrating on something else, something...dangerous. That was absurd. The only danger in that room was her unexplainable reaction to a man she'd just met. The danger lay in not knowing why he had such an effect on her, why she had allowed her mind to wander to the wondrous image of what it would be like to have him make love to her. She was dangerous—to herself!

"Josh," she said, resting her head on his shoulder once more.

"Hmm?"

"Nothing. I just wondered if anyone ever called you Joshua."

"No. Not anymore," he said quietly, his mind drifting back in time.

"Take the lighter, Joshua. Remember what it stands for. Remember who and what you are. You are a killer, and you can't change. Don't ever forget that, Joshua. Don't ever fool yourself into thinking you can change. Go. I'm dying. Go. Take the lighter, Joshua. And remember...remember..."

* * *

"Josh?"

"What?"

"Never mind. You just seemed to go off somewhere in your thoughts."

"I'm a heavy thinker," he said, smiling slightly.

"Do you suppose that's a sign of genius?"

"No doubt about it."

Kristin laughed softly, then reluctantly sat up, immediately missing the heat and strength that emanated from Josh.

"I'm very tired," she said. "It's been a long day. I'll get you some linens for the sofa. I'm afraid you're too tall for it, though."

"I'll be fine, and I appreciate your letting me stay."

She got to her feet and looked at him. "I guess...I guess we can't forget about that kiss, can we?"

"Do you want to?"

"I'm not sure.... Listen to me. I'm certainly making a lot of hoopla over what would be viewed by most people as an ordinary kiss."

"There was nothing ordinary about it." He took her hand and stroked his thumb over her knuckles. "I was part of that kiss, too, you know. It wasn't ordinary or simple. It was very special, very beautiful. I want to remember it.... I'm going to remember it. But you'll have to decide how to handle it. I won't mention it again unless you do."

"Oh, thanks," she said, smiling. "Dump it on me."

He released her hand and moved backward, spreading his arms along the top of the sofa as he grinned up at her.

"Well," he said, lifting one shoulder in a shrug, "I already know what I plan to do with my memory of it. I'm keeping it."

"I still say this is a lot of hoopla over one kiss."

Josh's expression became serious, and his voice was low when he spoke. "Is it?"

Kristin looked directly into his dark eyes and felt a flutter of desire deep within her. "No," she whispered, "maybe it isn't." She tore her gaze from his. "I'll get the pillow and blankets." She hurried from the room.

Josh watched her go, then pushed himself to his feet to stand closer to the fire. He took his cigarettes from his pocket and lighted one, then replaced the rather crumpled pack.

He closed his hand into a tight fist around his lighter, blocking it from his view. Memories assaulted him. Dark, evil memories. Cold memories. He pulled his mind from the past, rammed the lighter into his pocket and concentrated on the warming flames on the hearth.

And thought of Kristin.

The kiss.

The want.

The need.

And the emotion that had crept in around him as he'd held, touched and kissed her.

What in the hell was Kristin Duquesne doing to him?

Josh flicked the cigarette into the fire, then gripped the mantel with his large hands, exerting such force that his knuckles turned white. He needed, he knew, a physical release, needed to swim or run, to drive the tension from his body. But if he went running in the rain he'd have no reason to spend the night at Kristin's. Anyone nuts enough to jog in this weather could sleep in a house without heat.

He'd have to draw on the powers of his brain, he realized. He'd done it for years, knew how to master his body and mind, knew how to keep both under his command and control.

"Damn," Josh said, smacking the mantel with the palm of his hand. How was it possible that a whisper of a woman had knocked him so off track? He shouldn't have kissed her—he knew that now—and it wouldn't happen again. He wanted this assignment over with—fast!

"Here you go, Josh," Kristin said, coming back into the room. "Pillow, sheets, blanket, towel." She set them on the sofa.

"Thank you," he said, turning to face her.

"I'll say good-night now," she said. "Feel free to use the shower. I hope you sleep well."

"Thank you."

"Good night." She didn't move as their eyes met. She wanted him to kiss her again, didn't seem able to stop herself from wanting it. To be held in Josh's strong arms, feel his mouth on hers, give way to the desire smoldering within her... Yes, that was what she wanted.

Josh shoved his hands into his pockets to keep from hauling Kristin into his arms and covering her mouth with his. To keep from feeling her respond to him. To keep from making love to her.

"Good night, Kristin," he said, his voice husky. "I can't kiss you now. If I did, it wouldn't stop there, and you know it. I don't think you're ready to take that step with me, are you?''

Yes! "No," she whispered.

''Then good night.''

She nodded, then slowly walked away.

Damn it, Josh thought, hurry up! She had to get out of that room before he threw all his grand nobility and common sense out the window and went after her. Never in his life had he sent away a woman he wanted, burned for, ached for, the way he did for Kristin.

But he had to, he reasoned. He had no room for whatever strange feeling was twisting inside him, he thought as he started to make up his bed. He had no room for Kristin in his mind, his heart, his life or, God help him, his soul. Because he needed no one.

He was Joshua Quinn.

And he was alone.

He was a killer.

With a weary sigh he turned out the light, then tugged off his shoes. He heard the bathroom door close, then the sound of the shower. A short time later the water stopped.

Pictures of Kristin drying herself with a soft towel flitted before his eyes. Then the image of her floating some kind of feminine pajamas over her head. She'd smell like soap, he mused. Fresh, clean, all woman. She'd be in that pretty room of hers now, slipping into bed, maybe stretching like a lazy kitten as her hair fanned out on the pillow. Then she'd lift her arms to welcome him into her embrace and he'd—

''Why am I doing this to myself?'' he mumbled to the fire as he shifted his aroused body on the sofa.

"I'm taking on masochistic tendencies. Sick. Really sick."

Muttering a few well-chosen expletives, he laced his hands behind his head, continued to stare into the fire and waited. He had to find out if Kristin was a light sleeper. Half an hour later he picked up the towel she'd given him and went into the bathroom. He showered, dried off and pulled on his briefs and slacks. If Kristin had slept through the noise of the shower and the pounding rain, he was home free.

Josh opened the door leading to her bedroom and slipped inside, then soundlessly moved to the edge of the bed. He almost groaned as he saw, in the soft glow of light from the bathroom, the vision of loveliness in the bed.

Beautiful, he thought. Her hand was tucked gracefully by her cheek as she lay on her back, her hair spread out on the pillow just as he'd imagined it. The blankets were pulled up to just below her breasts, and her pajamas brought a smile to his lips. Kristin wasn't wearing some ultrafeminine peekaboo creation, but had on a faded football jersey. He could see the word Dallas and the beginning of the number; the rest was hidden under the blanket.

Josh stood by the bed and gazed at her for several more long minutes before moving away. As silently as he'd entered he left Kristin's room, picked up his shirt and socks from the bathroom, then turned out the light. Back in the living room, he waited until his eyes adjusted to the darkness. He reached into the pocket of his slacks.

There were five of them. Thin, no bigger than a dime. They represented big bucks and high technology, and he'd used them to his advantage in the past.

A knot tightened in his stomach as he realized that this time it was Kristin's privacy he was invading, Kristin's home, her safe haven, the place where she should feel most secure.

He had no choice, he told himself. He couldn't be with her every minute, and the metal disks in his hand would help give him the edge he needed. He'd place them in carefully chosen locations in the rooms. Then, when he turned on the device he had at the Jamesons' house, he'd be able to hear every word spoken within the walls of Kristin Duquesne's home.

Three

———

It came as no surprise to Kristin upon awakening the next morning that her first thought was of Josh. She had dreamed of Josh Quinn the entire night. Her fingertips came to rest on her lips as she experienced yet again the feeling of Josh's mouth on hers.

Enough, she told herself firmly. In the light of this new day she would get Josh and the previous evening's events back in perspective. She would see him as the attractive, extremely masculine man that he was but realize that he was just that—a man. A man on vacation from a high-pressure job. A man who would disappear from her life as quickly as he'd come.

Kristin threw back the blankets and headed for the bathroom. A short time later she was dressed in tan cords and a brown sweater. She pushed her feet into loafers, brushed her hair and applied lip gloss. A peek through the bedroom curtains revealed a blue sky, and sunshine glittered off the damp trees in the woods. Everything looked sparkling and clean after the rain.

If Josh was awake she would offer to fix him breakfast, she decided. They'd chat briefly, then he'd go to the Jamesons'. And that would be that. She had so much to do. She was eager to start sketching and painting, was behind in her correspondence and needed to straighten cupboards and drawers. During the following two months she would be the master of her own time, and it was an exhilarating feeling.

How would Josh spend his days? Where would he direct all the leashed power she could virtually feel emanating from him? Oh, for heaven's sake, it was none of her business. He was a temporary neighbor, nothing more.

Kristin nodded decisively, then left the bedroom and went down the hall to the living room. And then she stopped, statue-still, aware of the wave of disappointment that swept over her—and instantly angry at herself for having registered the emotion.

Josh was gone.

The bed linens were stacked neatly in the corner of the sofa, and she could see a note on top. She marched across the room and snatched up the paper, frowning as she read the simple "Thanks—Josh" written in bold, sprawling handwriting.

She stared at the note, then at the sofa, recalling what had transpired there with Josh. Feeling the warm flush that crept into her cheeks, she went quickly into the kitchen. Josh had made coffee, and it was still warm. With a mug of the reviving brew nestled in her hands, she sank onto a chair at the table.

Again memories of the previous night assaulted her. There'd been passion in Josh's kiss, she mused, and raw need. He had wanted her.

And, heaven help her, she'd wanted him.

Wonderful, she thought dryly. So much for getting everything into perspective in the light of the new day. If Josh walked through her door right that minute she'd probably leap into his arms.

"Oh, Kristin," she said, getting to her feet, "go make your bed."

Josh stood by the front window in the Jamesons' living room, every muscle tensed as he looked out at the woods through binoculars.

Two men so far, he thought. They were wearing heavy, dark jackets and carrying canvas bags. Each man occasionally picked up a twig and placed it in the bag. One man was tall and thin, pale, with white-blond hair. The other was shorter, burly, swarthy, and older than the baby face with him.

Josh glanced over at the small black box that sat on the desk against the wall. The box was equipped to send coded messages and receive replies and would transmit all conversations that took place in Kristin's house.

Josh gave the transmitter a hard stare, willing it to come alive, to tell him whether the descriptions of the men matched any on record in the central computer, to tell him whether Kristin was already in danger from the visitors in the woods.

What was taking his man on the other end so damn long? Josh fumed. He needed to know—now— whether there was a significant purpose behind the sudden appearance of those men near Kristin's house. His every instinct told him their arrival was no coincidence.

Josh redirected his attention to the binoculars and saw that the tall blond man had disappeared for the moment and that the other man was leaning against a tree. He wasn't looking for kindling, Josh realized. He was slowly scanning the street.

"Damn," he said aloud, looking at the black box again.

A small smile tugged at the corners of his mouth. Kristin talked to herself. Earlier he'd heard her tell herself to go make her bed. He'd registered a twinge of guilt for listening to her, but it couldn't be helped. He needed the edge that the black box gave him.

Kristin. So, yeah, okay, Josh admitted to himself, he'd looked in on her that morning as she'd slept. He'd done it with the sole purpose of proving to himself that while she was lovely, she wasn't extraordinary, wasn't enough to have caused him to toss and turn all night. But the glimpse of her in the glow of dawn's light hadn't done the job. She'd been even better than his memories of her from the previous evening.

And last night's kiss had been heaven itself....

A sudden bleep from the black box brought Josh out of his reverie, and he strode across the room. There was a crackling noise that, to an untrained ear, would have sounded like nothing more than static.

But Josh Quinn heard the steady rhythm of the coded message filtering through the grating surface noise. He heard and understood, and his jaw tightened as he narrowed his eyes.

The men were enemy agents with long lists of aliases. They'd just arrived from Paris.

"Damn," Josh said fiercely.

The message was repeated, Josh signaled that he understood, then returned to the window and his vigil with the binoculars.

His obsidian eyes as he watched the men in the woods were as cold as ice.

After lunch, Kristin put on her red parka and went outside, filling her lungs with the crisp, rain-washed air. To her own amazement, she'd had a very productive morning. She'd cleaned the house from front door to back and straightened closets and drawers, and was going to reward herself with an afternoon in her studio.

She had not appreciated the fact that thoughts of one Mr. Joshua Quinn had accompanied her as she'd done her chores, but no number of stiff lectures to herself had removed his image from her brain. She'd finally thrown up her hands in defeat and decided that if memories of Josh wanted to be on her mind while she scoured the bathtub, so be it.

As Kristin strolled down the street, she looked at the sidewalk, avoiding the mud puddles left by the heavy rain. When she neared the mailboxes she lifted her head, then stumbled slightly before continuing forward.

He was there, by the mailboxes.

Josh.

Tall and dark, massive in his sheepskin jacket, his hair tousled by the breeze. He was watching her approach, his expression unreadable. Just watching her. Kristin's heart began to beat a wild cadence.

She stopped in front of him and met his gaze.

Neither spoke. They stood as still as statues carved from ice. Burning ice.

Kristin's knees began to tremble.

Heat gathered heavy, deep, and low in Josh's body.

"Kristin," he said finally, nodding slightly.

That was all he said, but his rich, rumbly voice flowed over her and through her. Kristin had the irrational thought that she was going to dissolve into a heap at Josh's feet, her bones having melted from the intense gaze from those dark, dark eyes.

"Well," she said, much too loudly, "it's time to check the mail."

"I was chatting with the mailman," Josh said. "He put a couple of things in your box."

Kristin opened her box and pulled out two envelopes. "An electric bill and something for the occupant. That's not very exciting. Did you get what you were expecting?"

Damn it, he fumed, the package hadn't come. "No."

"Are your utilities on?"

"Yes, I'm all set. Thanks again for the use of the sofa." He paused. "I was just going to take a walk. Would you like to go? You might spot Magic Lady."

Kristin smiled. "All right. The wind is picking up. It's going to get chillier."

"Well, then, when we get back I'll tell myself that I deserve a brandy," he said, smiling at her. "Did you lock your house?"

"No, but it's not necessary."

"Humor me. We'll go back to your place, lock up and start our walk from there," he said. "Okay?"

Kristin shrugged. "Okay."

Good, Josh thought as they started down the street. This was exactly how he'd planned it. It was risky, but he had to chance it. The jokers in the woods had to have spotted Kristin's bright red jacket the moment she'd stepped out of her house. Now they would also see him and know they couldn't count on Kristin being alone. With any luck they'd peg him, realize that Josh Quinn was very much on the scene. If they were smart and watched him, they'd figure out he was staying at the house next to Kristin's and make a move on him to clear their path to her.

His hope was that they'd think Josh Quinn was slipping, didn't know he was a sitting duck, that they'd laugh themselves silly before they muscled in to take him out. Josh was just buying some time. Once he'd eliminated the two in the woods, they'd have to be replaced. By the time the enemy figured out the agents had been removed, Josh would already have the package.

Right, he thought dryly. It always sounded good on paper. Now all he had to do was get everyone to follow his script. But Kristin wasn't an actor in this play; she was a beautiful, innocent woman who wasn't even aware she had a role. A dangerous role. It was up to Josh to make sure he maintained the position of director, to make sure no one else took charge. It was up to him to keep Kristin Duquesne safe.

On the sidewalk directly in front of Kristin's house, Josh stopped to light a cigarette. He cupped his hand around the lighter to shield the flame from the wind, making certain that his face was clearly visible. The stage was set.

Except, he mused, for one extra little touch. Any agent worth his salt knew the dangers of becoming emotionally involved. That could make an agent blow a mission and even cost lives. The two in the woods might become wary of Josh's seemingly carefree willingness to be seen. It might serve a worthwhile purpose for Josh to make it appear that his mind was not on his assignment.

He took a deep drag off the cigarette, then slipped the lighter into his pocket. He could feel Kristin's presence next to him, was aware of her light floral perfume. He remembered the previous night with her and wished none of it tarnished. He wanted the kiss they'd shared, the feeling of her body pressed to his, the warmth, kept separate from who he was, from what he was doing there.

But what he wanted and what had to be done were not one and the same.

He forced a smile onto his face and turned to her. Then, as a knot tightened painfully in his stomach, he lifted his arm and circled her shoulders, pulling her close to his side.

"Body heat," he said, flashing his most dazzling smile. "You'll be credited with having kept me from freezing to death. Let's start walking before my toes turn to icicles."

Kristin laughed, and the sound was shaky to her own ears. She could hear the thread of nervousness in her voice. She considered wiggling out of Josh's embrace with a playful retort about the walk having been his idea, not hers. She considered it and rejected it in one beat of her racing heart. She was going to stay nestled close to him, she knew, and she wondered yet again about the strange power this man had over her.

They started down the street at a leisurely pace, Josh squinting against the rising smoke of his cigarette.

He could feel the men watching them. They would have powerful binoculars that wouldn't miss the smallest detail. They were looking at Kristin, every inch of her, and probably making crude remarks.

And he hated the very thought of it.

He wanted to grab them by their throats, slam them up against a wall, tell them in the language of violence to keep their filthy eyes and hands off her.

Because Kristin Duquesne was his!

Josh's step faltered for a moment. Kristin Duquesne was what? he asked himself. Where in the hell had that bizarre thought come from? Kristin was an assignment and not a damn thing more!

Kristin felt the tension building in Josh and glanced up at him. It had happened again, she realized. His eyes. The warmth from his smile was gone, replaced by the chill of eyes as dark as black ice. Where did his mind go? The tension from his body came in waves, taking him so very far away from her.

They reached the end of the street and turned to walk toward the business district of Temple.

"Josh?"

"Hmm?"

"Have you . . . have you decided how long you're going to stay here?"

"What?" he said, looking down at her. "Oh, no. I haven't really given it much thought. It feels great to be relaxed, not have a schedule to meet. I'd like to explore the town—and have a complete tour of your gallery, of course. I've never met a famous artist before.''

"I'm not exactly famous." Josh was smiling again, she thought incredulously. The smile reached his eyes, chasing away the chill.

Oh, the complexities of this man, she mused. And the secrets. Because, yes, there were secrets surrounding Josh Quinn. Secrets interwoven with an aura of danger. She wanted to dismiss the idea as her fanciful imagination. Wanted to, but couldn't.

"Now you're getting cold," Josh said. "I felt you shiver."

Not from the cold, Kristin thought, but from the tremor of fear that had swept through her and from the excitement that had come with it. And not to be ignored was the flicker of desire deep within her.

"We can turn back if you're cold, Kristin," Josh said.

"No, no, I'm fine. I'm used to this, you know. It gets much colder than today as winter settles in."

"Not my thing," he said, shaking his head.

"Oh, you'd get used to the cold in time."

"No," he said sharply. Kristin glanced up at him, a frown on her face. "What I mean," he added quickly, smiling down at her, "is I'd be a six-foot-three-inch ice pop before I made the adjustment to the weather. There I'd be, frozen stiff, until I defrosted in the spring."

Kristin laughed softly as they continued to walk. Nice try, but no cigar, she mused. That smile had not reached his eyes. His deep-seated aversion to the cold was far more than some general climate preference.

Good grief, what was she doing, playing amateur detective?

And she wanted Josh Quinn to kiss her again.

"Well, for Pete's sake," Kristin said, feeling a warm flush on her cheeks.

"What's wrong?"

"I… You're right. I am becoming chilled. I should be getting back anyway, because I plan to work in my studio this afternoon."

Josh stopped. "All right."

"I can go back alone, Josh, if you're still in the mood to walk."

"No, I'll see you safely home."

"Safely?" she said, smiling. "There's certainly nothing in this neighborhood to jeopardize my safety." Except her own wanton thoughts, she tacked on silently.

"Just a figure of speech," Josh said as they turned back. "I'm the old-fashioned type. I took you for a walk; I'll escort you safely home."

"Ah, I see," Kristin said, smiling. "Lessons learned at your mother's knee."

Josh's jaw tightened. "Something like that."

"Is that gold lighter you use a family heirloom?" she asked pleasantly.

"No."

"But it's important to you."

"It… it reminds me of who I am," he said quietly.

Kristin stopped walking and looked up at him. "Who are you, Josh?" she said softly.

"I've told you."

"No, there's more. There's something you're not telling me."

Damn, Josh raged, he'd blown it again! He couldn't believe this. "You're reading too much into what I said, Kristin." If one of my men were screwing up this badly, I'd nail him to the wall. "Look, the lighter is like a lucky penny or a rabbit's foot, that's all. I didn't mean to make it sound so dramatic."

"Oh," she said, nodding slowly.

"Could we keep moving? I'm freezing." He pulled her closer to his side.

"Of course."

They walked in silence for several minutes until Kristin's house came into view.

"I know what I'm in the mood for," Kristin said. "A mug of hot chocolate with whipped cream on top. Care to join me? Or you could have that brandy you promised yourself."

"I haven't had hot chocolate in years."

"I make it from scratch," she said, trying to tempt him.

"Sold."

As they turned to walk up to Kristin's porch, Josh took a quick glance toward the woods. He couldn't see the men at the moment, but they were there, damn them.

Inside the house, Kristin hung up her coat and Josh draped his across the back of a chair. He was wearing a burgundy sweater and blue jeans, and Kristin's heart did a little tap dance as she watched him.

"Would you like me to start a fire?" he said.

In her or on the hearth? Kristin thought. Shame on her! "That would be nice. I'll make the hot chocolate." She went into the kitchen.

Kristin measured the ingredients into a pan, then began to stir the liquid over a low flame. She glanced up as Josh passed through the kitchen on his way to the laundry room for wood, and then again when he retraced his steps, his arms now full of logs.

How right he looked in her home, Kristin mused, staring into the pan. At first he'd seemed to overwhelm the space, hardly leaving her room to move or breathe. But now she felt comfortable with him there. As though he belonged there with her. Would he think that her bedroom, with its white eyelet bedspread and curtains, was too frilly and feminine? Her bedroom? Josh wasn't going to be in her bedroom.... Or was he?

"Stir, Kristin," she mumbled as the liquid began to bubble.

A short time later she carried a tray with two mugs of hot chocolate and a plate of cookies into the living room. Mounds of whipped cream floated on top of the steaming drinks.

"Thank you," Josh said, accepting a mug. "This looks great." He sat down on the center cushion of the sofa.

Kristin sat next to him, and their thighs brushed as she eased herself carefully into place so as not to spill her chocolate. She blew on the top, then took a sip.

"I just realized, Josh," she said, "that I don't even know where you live."

"I have an apartment in Washington, D.C., but I'm rarely there. Most of my training was done there, but for years now I've been away more than I've been home."

"Don't you get tired of all the traveling, living out of a suitcase?"

Living in jungles, he added silently, in the hot spots of the world, the troubled areas, where someone was usually trying to kill him to keep him from carrying out his assignment.

"Yeah," he said, nodding, "lately I've found myself thinking that it might be nice to settle in one place." He really had been giving it some thought, he admitted. He was getting tired of it all, just so damn tired.

"What would you do if you weren't a trouble-shooter for a computer company?"

"Teach," he said. Teach new agents how to survive in the darkness out there; share his expertise; give them the edge they'd need to stay alive. "I'd have a normal nine-to-five job."

"That's nice," Kristin said, sliding him a quick glance. Very, very nice, she mused dreamily.

Just as Kristin took another sip of chocolate, a log in the fireplace broke, landing with a sharp bang and sending sparks dancing against the screen. Kristin jumped a bit, jiggling her cup. The whipped cream slid to the edge of the mug and covered her upper lip and the area under her nose.

She laughed. "Oh, dear, I'd better go get a napkin."

"No," Josh said, his voice low.

He reached across her to set his mug on the end table, then took Kristin's and placed it next to his. He moved his hand to the nape of her neck and leaned toward her as she watched him, her eyes wide.

"Josh, what—"

"Shhh," he said. "We can't waste real whipped cream, can we?"

"I . . . well . . ."

He slid his tongue slowly over her upper lip, and a shiver of desire swept through her. Then, with maddening precision, he sucked gently, inching his way along her lip—licking, tasting, pulling the softness into his mouth.

Kristin trembled. Heat curled deep within her, and she gripped Josh's shoulders for support as she closed her eyes. Sensations rocketed through her, and her breasts grew heavy and achy. Josh was concentrating only on her upper lip, yet she felt as though every inch of her were branded by his glorious touch.

But she wanted more! So much more.

"Josh, please. Kiss me," she whispered. "Really kiss me."

He claimed her mouth, and his tongue plunged deep within. He tasted like chocolate and whipped cream and Josh, and Kristin met his tongue eagerly, circling his neck with her arms. He pulled her close, letting his hands roam over her back, pressing her breasts to the unyielding wall of his chest. Without lifting his mouth from hers, he slid his large hands under her sweater, then up over her silken skin to the sides of her breasts.

"Kristin?" he said, his voice raspy. "I want to see you."

"Yes."

He moved her away just enough to remove her sweater and bra, which he dropped onto the floor. He swept his smoldering gaze over her breasts, and with visibly shaking hands he filled his palms with her. With his thumbs he stroked her nipples until they were taut buttons.

"Lovely," he said. "Like ivory velvet."

He dipped his head and drew one nipple deep into his mouth, sucking rhythmically. Heat gathered low in his body, arousing him, announcing his need and want of her. He moved to the other breast, and his breathing became rough.

How he wanted her, his mind hummed. His body was throbbing, aching, and with his physical need came that unknown emotion, taunting him from the shadows of his hazy thoughts.

A soft sigh of pleasure escaped from Kristin's throat. She reached for Josh's sweater and inched it upward with fumbling fingers. He lifted his head, drew his sweater up and off and flung it onto the floor.

"Oh, Josh," Kristin said, placing her hands flat on his tanned, muscled chest.

She wove her fingers through the dark curls, and he sucked in his breath as she found his nipples. She leaned forward, drawing lazy circles with the tip of her tongue as he groaned deep in his chest.

Josh gripped her head with his hands and tilted it upward, then brought his mouth down hard on hers in a searing kiss that seemed to steal the very breath from Kristin's body. She leaned into him, glorying in the sensation of her bare breasts on his hard chest. Deep within her, heat pulsed with a sweet pain.

How she wanted this man.

"Kristin," Josh said, his voice gritty with passion, "I want you. I want to make love to you. Now. Right now."

"Yes," she said, looking at him through half-closed eyes. "I want you, too. I trust you, Josh, just as you asked me to."

Kristin's words slammed against Josh's brain, and he went still, hardly breathing. He tried desperately to sort through his jumbled thoughts.

Kristin trusted him, a little voice repeated over and over. Yes, of course. He'd made sure of that because of the assignment, because— No! Her trust was a precious gift, just as her giving herself to him would have been. Her trust, the essence of who she was, had to be cherished, protected—not just her body.

He couldn't make love to this beautiful, delicate, trusting woman while she believed him to be other than what he really was. She had waited so long to trust again, and he wouldn't be the one to shatter her. She was too special.

"Kristin," he said, gently gripping her upper arms, "listen to me." He reached down for her sweater and bra and handed them to her, seeing the confusion on her face as she looked at him. He quickly drew on his own sweater.

"I want you," he said. "You know I do. But this isn't the time. You said you trust me, and that means so much to me. Please, trust me a while longer. I can't make love to you now. I just can't. Later I'll explain everything. I promise. But for now... Can you do it? Give me more time, more trust?"

Kristin clutched her sweater to her breasts to cover her nakedness and gazed directly into Josh's eyes. She heard the sincerity in his voice, the almost pleading undertones. Josh had called a halt to their lovemaking when she would have gone further, and she felt very special and cherished.

"Yes," she said softly. "I don't understand why you... but yes, I'll trust you."

He pulled her close and held her for a long moment. "Thank you." He kissed her on the forehead. "Put your sweater on," he said, smiling at her, "before I forget all my good intentions." He got to his feet and walked to the window, allowing her the privacy he sensed she needed at that moment.

Kristin quickly put on her bra and sweater, then ran her fingers through her tousled hair. Desire still thrummed within her, and she drew a deep, steadying breath.

She didn't understand why Josh had called a halt to the lovemaking, she admitted, but she did trust him. Why, she wasn't sure, but trusting Josh felt . . . right. There was a quiet message from her heart that told her that he should have the trust he was asking of her. And so she'd wait until he was ready to explain what he couldn't, or wouldn't, tell her now.

"Hey," Josh said from the window, "here's some good news for you. Magic Lady is strolling down the sidewalk."

Kristin thought for a moment, then spun around to look at Josh's back. "What did you say?"

He turned to look at her. "Magic Lady is—Kristin, what's wrong? You're white as a ghost."

She got to her feet, her knees starting to shake as she walked around the end of the sofa, then stopped. "Last night, when you first came here, you didn't even know that Magic Lady was a cat. How . . . how could you possibly know what she looks like? I never mentioned that she was black-and-white. How did you know that was her out there?"

Damn it to hell! Josh raged. He'd blown it!

"Oh, God," Kristin said, her voice quavering. "Who are you? What do you want with me? Why are you here?" A tremor of fear swept through her, and there was a roar in her ears. "Go away. Please, just go away and leave me alone."

"Kristin, please, calm down," he said, taking a step toward her.

"Don't come near me," she said, backing up. "This isn't funny anymore. This isn't exciting and intriguing like something out of a novel. It's frightening, and you have no right to do this to me."

Josh closed the distance between them and gripped her by the upper arms. His heart thundered in his chest when he saw the fear in her eyes, felt the trembling in her body.

"Kristin, listen to me. I'm not going to hurt you. You've got to believe that. I'm here to protect you, not harm you."

"Protect me? From what? This is insane. I want you to leave my home. Now. I'll phone the police and tell them—"

"Kristin, stop it," he said, giving her a small shake. "I'll explain everything to you, but I can't until you've calmed down. Come sit by the fire, and I'll get you a brandy."

"No."

"You can walk to the sofa or be carried. Take your pick."

Kristin pulled out of his grasp and marched to the sofa. She sat down, crossed her arms over her breasts and glowered at him.

"Man, oh, man," Josh said. He strode into the kitchen and returned with two snifters of brandy.

Kristin accepted hers and set it on the end table without looking at him.

Josh took a deep swallow of the liquor, then put the snifter on the mantel and stared at Kristin. Now what? He wasn't authorized to tell Kristin a thing. Despite his rank, he would have to get clearance to divulge the nature of his assignment. He'd told Kristin he would tell her everything so she would calm down. He'd have to go to the Jamesons', encode a message and wait for the reply giving him permission to proceed. Permission that might very well be denied. If the honchos ran true to form, he'd be instructed to keep his mouth shut and "work around the situation." Hell.

Kristin looked so frightened, he thought. She didn't deserve this. She was sunshine, laughter and warmth. She didn't belong in the cold darkness of the world he'd brought crashing into her life. *He* had put the fear in her beautiful eyes, on her lovely face, and only he could ease those fears.

From deep inside him, from the center of the unnamed emotion, came a quiet, gentle voice.

Tell her. Tell her, because she was more important than orders and authorization. Because the fear she was living with was cutting through him like the burning blade of a knife. Tell her, because she was Kristin.

"Kristin," he said, "look at me."

She slowly shifted her gaze to meet his. The knife within Josh twisted.

"My name really is Josh Quinn," he said quietly. "I'm an agent for the United States government." A killer. "Through no fault of your own you've been caught in the middle of a very dangerous situation. I was sent here to protect you and to see that a complicated plan that began many, many months ago comes to its proper end. I have identification at the Jamesons' that can verify that I *am* a government agent. I'm not here to hurt you. I swear it.''

Kristin continued to look at him, her face blank. Josh dragged a restless hand through his hair, then lit a cigarette.

He was blowing his career straight to hell, he thought. He didn't have the authority to tell her a thing, and they'd let him know by showing him the door. All those years, all those lives, for nothing.

But this was Kristin.

And he couldn't bear the pain of her fear.

''Your uncle Henri,'' he said, his voice suddenly weary, ''wasn't killed in the war. He was a reckless, wild young man but, in spite of that, was a top-notch intelligence officer. In later years he became a double agent, working for us but giving the impression he was anti-American. Through a very complicated plan he was able to obtain a microdot containing blueprints for a missile to be built by a foreign enemy. Before Henri could make his rendezvous with our agent he realized he was dying. In his panic he mailed the microdot to you.''

''What?'' Kristin whispered.

''That's why I'm here. I had hoped to get the package and leave without your ever knowing about it. Obviously it's too late for that. My job now is to protect you, make it very clear that I, not you, have the package, then lead those who want it away from you by getting them to come after me. Or get them to move on me before the package arrives. There are two men out there in the woods who are enemy agents. They want the package. They're not going to get it. And they're not going to hurt you."

"My God," Kristin said, pressing her hands to her pale cheeks, "this is a nightmare. I can't believe this. My uncle was alive all those years, now he's really dead, you're an agent for the government and there are men out there who want to—"

"Kristin, don't." Josh hunkered down in front of her and pulled her hands away from her face, enclosing them in both of his. "I know it's a lot to grasp all at once, and I realize it's very frightening. But I'm here, and I'm not going to let anything happen to you. Understand?"

Kristin stared at him for a long moment, then lifted her chin. "I presume you receive orders for these types of things."

"Yes," he said, confused.

"Written orders?"

"Sometimes. Why? What are you getting at?"

"I just wondered," she said, sudden tears misting her eyes, "in which paragraph it said to kiss me and hold me. And what else, Josh? How dedicated are you? Was there another clause in your orders that said to stay close to me at all costs until you got that package? You called a halt to our lovemaking today, but what about next time? Would you have done it, Josh? Would you have made love to me, all in the line of your damnable duty? Dear God in heaven, what kind of a man are you?"

Four

——

Josh pushed himself to his feet and turned to face the fire, moving closer to its heat. Never, never before, had he felt so cold, so incredibly empty. Kristin's words beat against his mind, giving no quarter. He had to convince her that what they had shared had been real and honest, not part of some master plan to win her trust.

Why was it so important that she believe him? he asked himself. Why did it matter? He didn't know, any more than he knew why he'd broken every rule in the book by telling her what was happening to her.

He turned slowly to face her. "Kristin," he said, his voice low, "what happened between us had nothing to do with why I came to stay at the Jamesons'. Yes, I had to meet you, get close to you so I could protect you, but I'd already done that. I was here in your home."

Her head snapped up, her eyes angry. "For the night. Dear heaven, I even allowed you to spend the night."

"During which," he said, a muscle jumping along his jaw, "I *could* have been in your bed, making love to you."

"Damn you," she said, jumping to her feet. "How dare you say such a thing!"

"Do you deny that you wanted me? You shared equally in what took place between us, responded to me totally, just as I did to you. I could have made love to you last night, and this afternoon, Kristin. Admit it."

Josh closed the distance between then and gripped her wrists. She made no attempt to yank her hands from his grasp. She looked up at him, tears welling up in her eyes.

"Listen to me," he said, his voice gentling, his heart thudding in his chest. "Think about what happened. Josh Quinn the man kissed you. And Josh Quinn the man called a halt. When we make love, Kristin, it's going to be by mutual agreement. It will have nothing to do with what's happening beyond this house. It will just be the two of us, man and woman. That was who we were when we shared what we did. I swear it. It was honest and real and very, very beautiful. I'm asking you to believe me."

Kristin swallowed the sob in her throat and stared at Josh, searching for the truth, for the answer she so desperately needed. A soft gasp escaped her lips when she looked into his dark eyes.

Dear God, it was as though he were standing naked before her. In his eyes was a vulnerability she had never seen there before. And she saw pain, raw and real. In that moment he was stripping away his defenses, begging her to believe him. No man could evoke such emotions at will. Joshua Quinn was telling the truth.

Tears slid down her cheeks.

"Kristin, please," Josh said, his voice raspy.

"I...I believe you, Josh," she whispered. "I believe that you held and kissed me as a man, nothing more. I do."

He pulled her roughly to him, circling her body with his arms and burying his face in her fragrant, silken hair.

"Thank you," he murmured. "Thank you, Kristin."

For a long moment he held her, simply held her. Kristin rested her head on his chest, savoring his strength and heat, pushing aside her fears and relishing the feel and aroma of Josh. She drew a shaky breath, then lifted her head to look up at him. The questions, the fears, began to creep in around her as her mind replayed all that he had told her.

"Josh, I—"

"Nothing is going to happen to you," he said fiercely. "Nothing."

He wove his fingers through her hair to hold her head, then lowered his lips to hers. The kiss was gentle, soft, sensuous. Then, as Kristin raised her arms to circle his neck, the kiss intensified. Tongues met and passions soared. All was forgotten but the sensations rushing through them. All was forgotten but the want and need.

Kristin leaned into his embrace, answering the demands of his mouth, feeling the evidence of his arousal pressing against her. She filled her senses with him.

Josh drank of Kristin's sweetness as he explored every crevice of her mouth with his tongue. Nestling her soft curves to his heated, aching body, he envisioned what it would be like to lift Kristin into his arms, carry her to the bedroom, then slowly remove her clothes to kiss every inch of her dewy skin. Their joining would be like none before, their becoming one a celebration of her femininity and his masculinity. She would be his.

Josh reluctantly lifted his head. "Kristin," he said, his voice harsh with passion, "we have to talk."

No! her mind screamed as she opened her eyes. No, she didn't want to hear about the nightmare lurking beyond her front door. She just wanted to stay in the safe haven of Josh's arms.

"Kristin," he said, gently setting her away from him.

"Yes, I know," she said, her voice trembling. "I know, but it's all so frightening and—"

"Shhh," he said, taking her hand. "Come sit with me on the sofa."

She sighed. "All right."

Kristin sat down, and Josh settled next to her, shifting to face her. He stroked his thumb over her cheek before laying his arm along the back of the sofa.

"I realize that what I told you is hard to grasp all at once," he said. "The important things are that you're kept safe and that we get that package. I'm going to have to ask you to follow my instructions to the letter.''

"I understand," she said, nodding.

"In this house—" he stopped and ran his hand over the back of his neck "—are hidden listening devices.''

"What?" she said, her eyes widening.

"It's for your safety. When I'm over at the Jamesons' I can hear everything that's taking place here.''

"That's an invasion of my privacy. That's—''

"An edge. Something in our favor. I want them to come after me first to get me out of the way. I have to be where they can get to me, over at the Jamesons'. But while I'm there I can keep track of what's going on here," he explained.

"You're going to be in danger, Josh.''

"Not really. I'll be prepared for them. I'm hoping they recognized me on the sidewalk, know they have to deal with me first. I'm also hoping..." His voice trailed off.

"Yes?"

"Kristin, that I made myself so visible to them is out of character for the way I operate. When I put my arm around you as we were walking, it was to give the impression that I'm becoming emotionally involved with you, getting sloppy as an agent. I'm admitting to you that I set up that scenario outside. That doesn't change what we've shared in this house. Do you believe that?''

Kristin looked directly into his eyes. "Yes."

"Thank you."

"What happens now?"

"We wait. They want the package. They'd prefer to get it without involving you at all, just as I would. Maybe...maybe you could go away for a few days. It wouldn't be unusual to ask a neighbor to bring in your mail while you're on a trip. The mailman knows who I am now."

"No."

"No?"

"If you think I'm going off while some men are skulking around out there, waiting to attack you, you're crazy. If you're supposed to be involved with me, why would I up and leave? They'd know you were expecting trouble and had sent me away. Wouldn't it be better for them to think they're catching you off guard?"

"Well, yes, but you'd be safer away from here."

"No," she said, crossing her arms.

"Damn," Josh said, raking a hand through his hair. "What happened to your following my instructions?"

"Josh, my uncle was involved in this. He sent that package to me. I can't ignore the fact that the Duquesne name is very much a part of this. I thought I was the only one left—well, now I really am—but all those years my uncle was alive, doing important things for this country. My parents never knew the man my uncle really was, never had a chance to be proud of him. It must have broken my father's heart to pretend that his brother was dead to keep me from knowing that a Duquesne was disgracing us, or whatever they thought he was doing."

"Henri made sure they thought that. He sacrificed his family, you and your parents, to maintain his cover."

"Oh, Josh, don't you see? I can't walk away from this. I'm the only one remaining. I owe it to my parents and to my uncle to see that this is finished the way it was meant to be. If I don't, all those years they were lost to each other will have been for nothing."

"I hear what you're saying, Kristin, and I respect what you're trying to do. But, damn it, it's not worth putting your own life in jeopardy!"

Kristin shrugged. "So protect me."

Josh uttered an earthy expletive and got to his feet. He paced in front of the fireplace, then stopped, frowning at her.

"They'll stop at nothing to get that package, Kristin. This isn't a game we're playing here."

"I realize that. When is the package supposed to arrive? I assume that since you're here it's due anytime."

"Yes."

"Josh, how are you going to let them know that you have it instead of me?"

"They don't want me to get it. They'll want me out of the way, hope to get to your mailbox before you do and leave with the package with you never being the wiser. Their first plan will be to not involve you, a private citizen, although they're not beyond stealing your mail."

"And their second plan?"

"Up front? They'll do whatever is necessary to get what they're after. Don't you see, Kristin? You're in potential danger."

"Not if you get them first. Isn't that what you intend to do?"

"Well, yeah, but things don't always go the way I'd like them to. I have the advantage at the moment, but... Kristin, pack a suitcase. I'm getting you out of here."

"No."

"Hell," he said, throwing up his hands.

"When do you think they'll come after you, Josh?"

He looked at her for a long moment. "Tonight."

Kristin shivered. "Oh."

"They can't afford to waste any more time."

"I see," she said quietly. She stared at the ceiling with narrowed eyes. "Josh," she said, looking at him again, "what if they thought I couldn't get to my mailbox?"

"What do you mean?"

"Well, we're supposed to be lovers or...something, right?"

Josh nodded. "That's the impression I was trying to give outside."

"Lovers often have quarrels. We're in here right now arguing, and I get so upset I run out the door and down the stairs of the porch. But—" she pointed a finger in the air "—I slip, twist my ankle. You come charging after me and have to carry me back. Now I'm out of the picture. The only thing standing between them and my mailbox is you. I can stay here, where I belong, and not be in any danger." She smiled brightly. "Get it?"

Josh glared at her.

"Of course," she went on, "I'm not crazy about the idea of those men coming after you, but I have to believe that you're trained to handle things like this. I won't leave my home, Josh, but I will do whatever is necessary to keep out of your way. If I can't walk to my mailbox, I can't possibly get the package. They'll have no reason to come near me, and you'll be free to do...whatever it is you have to do.'' She swallowed heavily. ''I don't want to think about that part. You will be careful, won't you? I mean, you won't be hurt or—'' Her voice faltered.

Josh sat down next to her and took her hand. ''Nothing is going to happen to me, Kristin. If you won't leave here, then I guess your plan isn't all that bad. It would be an extra safety feature to ensure that they'd have no reason to come near you. They'd definitely think they only had to get rid of me to have clear access to the package. Plus, if we quarreled, it would explain why I went to the Jamesons' tonight instead of staying here with you. You've hurt your ankle but can hobble around enough to move through the house, so you sent me packing.''

''Right.''

''It's risky. If I leave you alone, they'll assume you can get to the kitchen for food, then make it to your bed. We have to hope they'll decide you won't take on the walk down the block to get your mail.''

''I could limp out there tomorrow, look down the street, then change my mind.''

''By tomorrow, with any luck, this should all be over. I'm counting on them making their move on me tonight.''

''Oh,'' she said in a small voice, ''that's right. Every time I think about that part I get chills. Oh, Josh, please, promise me you'll be careful.''

He looked at her intently. "You really mean that, don't you? You really care."

"Yes, I care," she said softly, meeting his gaze. "I don't...I don't understand what's happening between us, Josh, and I don't have any room for it right now. This other thing is so big, so frightening. Yes, I care, but I can't examine it any closer at the moment. Does that make sense?"

He nodded. "Yes. Yes, it makes perfect sense, because I'm in the same place. Nothing like this, like you, has ever happened to me. I've already broken so many rules— Never mind."

"Rules? What rules have you broken?"

"Don't worry about it. And, yes, I promise that I'll be careful. When this is over we'll..." His voice trailed off. They'd what? he asked himself. Make love? Get in touch with themselves to see what was happening between them? Would he still be alone, because he wouldn't know how to allow her to really touch him?

"Josh?"

"We'll talk," he said. "We'll talk when it's all over."

Josh claimed Kristin's mouth with unhurried pleasure, allowing desire to simmer within him as he met her tongue and tasted her sweetness. He cleared his mind of all rational thought.

He moved his hands beneath her sweater to skim over her soft skin. He remembered the feel of her lush breasts as he'd taken each in turn with his mouth, and the blood pounded low in his body as he ached with the desire to suckle them once more. The need for her was consuming him, his desire to make love to her greater than any he had ever known.

Kristin returned the kiss with total abandon, giving to him, receiving from him, the sensual promise of what could be. Yearning pulsed deep within her, twisting, churning, tightening with liquid fire. Her breasts ached for Josh's touch, for his mouth, for the glorious sensations his tongue and lips had created as they'd taken possession of her soft flesh. The blood hummed in her veins, and her heart raced. She savored the sweet ache of wanting more, of wanting Josh, and leaned farther into his strength and heat.

Josh lifted his head, his breathing rough. "Kristin," he said, his voice gritty, "no more. Not now."

"Hmm?" she said dreamily.

"Kristin."

She opened her eyes. "Yes?"

"Don't look at me like that," he said gruffly.

"Oh," she said, straightening and blinking several times. "Well, then, don't kiss me like that."

He chuckled. "Point taken." In the next moment he was serious. "Are you ready to do your award-winning job of acting?"

"I—" She drew a steadying breath. "I don't know if I can get into the role of having just quarreled with you."

"I know what you mean. I shouldn't have kissed you, I guess. Damn, I wish you'd reconsider and just go away until this is over."

"No."

He sighed. "I didn't think so. Okay, let's do it. You run out the door, go down the stairs, then pretend to twist your ankle at the bottom."

"Right." She placed her hand over her heart. "I think I'm scared to death. No, I'm not. I can handle this. Do I put on my coat? No, guess not. If I'm mad as blue blazes at you, I wouldn't stop to put on my coat. Wonderful. I'll probably catch pneumonia—all in the line of duty. Well, that's the way it goes. I—''

"Kristin—"

"Can you carry me back in here? Sure you can. You have marvelous muscles. Your whole body, in fact, is just super-duper and—"

"Kristin, you're babbling."

"I don't babble." She threw up her hands. "Now I do, I guess. I was definitely babbling."

"Let's just forget this screwball idea."

"No, no, it's a terrific plan," she said, getting to her feet. "Are you ready?"

Josh stood. "No."

"Tough. I'm on my way. I've never flounced out the door in a snit before."

"Not even when you broke your engagement?" Josh asked quietly.

Kristin's eyes widened. "You know about that?"

He nodded. "I read a brief file that was put together on you. It wasn't much, just a sketchy outline."

"Knowing you were briefed on me is rather disconcerting," she said, frowning.

"Necessary is a better word. What happened, Kristin? Why did you break your engagement so close to your wedding?" Josh said. Why was he asking her this now? he wondered. Better to get this scene outside over with. But suddenly he wanted, needed, to know. "Do you mind telling me?"

"It was a long time ago, and not that interesting. I trusted, and thought I loved, the wrong man, that's all. I found him in bed with someone else. And, no, I didn't exit stage left in a loud, angry tirade. I simply walked away without saying a word, canceled my wedding plans and never spoke to him again.''

''I'm sorry.''

''So was I. It took a long time for me to trust again.''

''But now you do?'' he said, his voice low.

Kristin looked into his ebony eyes. ''Yes.''

He trailed his thumb over her cheek. ''Thank you.''

They held their gazes, sending and receiving messages that were neither clearly defined nor totally understood. Josh was the first to break the spell.

''Let's get this show over with,'' he said, taking a step backward.

''All right,'' Kristin said, nodding.

She went to the door, looked once more at Josh, then flung the door open. She started to run, heading for the stairs, then hurrying down them, oblivious to the cold.

Josh waited, every muscle in his body tensed, as he forced himself to count slowly.

''Five,'' he said, then bolted after her.

When Kristin reached the bottom step, she shrieked, then tumbled to the ground, immediately grasping her right ankle with both hands. Josh came thundering across the porch and down the stairs. Kristin stumbled to her feet, took a step forward, then fell again.

''Kristin!'' Josh yelled, hurrying to her. He dropped to one knee beside her.

''Go away, you—you brute,'' she said, flailing her arms in the air. ''Go away. Go away.'' She made a fist with every intention of rendering a solid punch to Josh's chest.

She missed.

Her fist connected with his eye.

"Ow! Damn!" he said, teetering slightly.

"Oh, I'm so sorry," she said, her eyes wide. "Oh, what have I done? Does it hurt?"

"Stay mad, damn it," he growled. "You're dangerous. Get up, then sit right back down, gripping your ankle."

"Okay," she said, then did as instructed.

Josh scooped her up in his arms. "Push against my chest as though you're trying to get away. This is ridiculous. It really is. Oh, my eye."

"I'm so sorry."

"Would you please look angry?"

"You bet," she said, shoving at his chest. "How's this?"

"Terrific," he muttered, then started back up the stairs.

Josh carried her across the porch, then entered the house and kicked the door closed behind him. He plopped her rather unceremoniously on the sofa, then gingerly probed his eye with his fingertips.

"I'm sorry about your eye," Kristin said, wringing her hands.

Josh laughed. "You pack quite a wallop, kid. The government could use you as a secret weapon."

"How did I do?"

"It was an Academy Award-winning performance."

"Really?" she said, smiling brightly.

He sank onto the sofa next to her. "Really. I felt like an idiot. I've never chased after an irate woman in my life."

"Oh?" she said, leaning toward him. "Known a lot of them, have you? You're in the habit of making women angry?"

"Me?" he said, covering his heart with his hand. "Lovable me? Don't be silly."

"Josh, your eye is swelling."

"Great," he said, getting to his feet. "That's all I need. I'll put some ice on it."

Lovable? Kristin thought as he went into the kitchen. As in capable of being loved, of having a woman fall in love with him? As in Kristin Duquesne falling in love with Joshua Quinn? No, she wouldn't even entertain the thought now, not now.

Josh returned with a towel pressed to his eye and sat down next to her again.

"I'll stay a few more minutes," he said, "then go stomping down the sidewalk to Jamesons'. You stay inside and keep the curtains closed. When it gets dark, use the lights, but don't move from one room to the next too quickly. You're trying to give the impression that you can't walk very well. I'm hoping none of this playacting will have been necessary. I realize it might be tempting to talk out loud because you know I can hear you through the listening devices, but don't do it. I might have company. If you were chattering away to me it would be obvious that you know exactly what is going on."

"I understand. Oh, Josh, this is going to be so difficult. I'll be sitting here wondering what's happening over at the Jamesons'. This may very well be the longest night of my life.''

She cares, Josh's heart echoed over and over. She truly cares. "I'll be fine, Kristin," he said. "I'll be back as soon as . . . well, as soon as I can. Don't go outside under any circumstances. Understand?''

"Yes.''

"Hey, don't look so scared." He pulled her close. "Anyone with a right cross like yours is a tough number. This will all be over by morning." He hoped.

"I'm all right. I just don't want anything to happen to you, Josh.''

He set the towel on the floor, then claimed her mouth in a fiery kiss. She was trembling when he finally released her.

"See you soon," he said close to her lips. "Lock up after I leave.''

Josh got to his feet and Kristin followed, walking beside him to the door.

"Keep out of sight," he said. "You're mad as hell, remember? And your ankle hurts. You wouldn't see me to the door." He shrugged into his jacket. "You're doing great, Kristin. Just hang on a little longer. Okay?''

"Yes," she said, managing a weak smile. "I'll—I'll be waiting for you, Josh.''

Josh frowned slightly, then brushed his lips over hers. In the next instant he was gone.

Kristin stood in the quiet room, wrapping her hands around her elbows in a protective gesture. Josh had slammed the door as he'd left to emphasize his phony anger, but now there was only silence. Screaming silence.

The events of the past hours piled up, one onto the next, like building blocks of emotions too heavy for Kristin to bear. Tears welled up in her eyes and spilled unnoticed onto her cheeks as she stood alone and lonely in the quiet room.

Josh strode along the sidewalk, giving, he hoped, the impression that he was an angry and frustrated man who had just endured a nasty quarrel with his lady.

Part of him was very aware of the woods, of their aura of danger and of the two men he knew to be hiding in the trees.

But another part of Josh Quinn was hearing over and over the softly spoken words of Kristin Duquesne. ''I'll be waiting for you, Josh.''

Never before, he realized, had anyone waited for him, cared if he returned. God, it felt good.

Josh entered the Jamesons' house, took off his jacket and tossed it onto a chair. He planted his hands on his hips and stared up at the ceiling, drawing a deep breath.

Well, he might as well get it over with. He was due to report in, and with his update would go the information that he'd told Kristin Duquesne the details of a top-secret government operation.

Josh moved to the black box and sent a coded message that stated, ''No package. Foreign agents still in woods. K.D. has been apprised of entire situation as it stands.''

Short and sweet, Josh thought dryly. He'd just signed his own pink slip. He'd been thinking about getting out of the agency, but not like this, not after all those years. But if he had it to do over again, he'd still tell Kristin everything.

Because she'd been so frightened. Because she trusted him. Because she cared.

For the next half hour Josh paced around the room, stopping often to look at the woods through the binoculars. He saw the men once as they conversed in the shadows of the trees. The tall man nodded, and then they disappeared in opposite directions.

The black box beeped. The coded reply to his message said simply, "Wait for phone call."

"Wonderful," he muttered, then resumed his pacing, stopping at regular intervals to watch the woods.

An hour later the telephone rang.

Josh grabbed up the receiver. "Yeah?"

"Is Jeff there?" a man asked. "Jeff Jameson?"

"No, he isn't here."

"Damn, he's not at his place, either. I thought he might have gone to visit his folks. Listen, if he calls, could you give him a message?"

"Yeah, sure," Josh said, running his hand over the back of his neck.

"This is Joe. Tell Jeff I thought it over and decided to tell Judy the truth about what I did. Man, what a mistake that was. But what's done is done. I figure this calls for a little faith here. I have to believe I did the right thing, and I'm not going to put myself through hell about it. Only time will tell if I was wrong. Make sense?"

"Yeah," Josh said, nodding. "Sometimes the truth is the only road to go. I'm betting that you won't be sorry."

"I hope you're right. There's a lot at stake here. Anyway, tell Jeff if you talk to him, okay?"

"Yeah, I will."

"Thanks, buddy."

Josh slowly replaced the receiver. Well, well, he thought, very interesting. They weren't going to land on him with both feet for telling Kristin what was going on. They didn't like it, but they were willing to believe in Josh to the point that they'd give him the benefit of the doubt and wait and see how things turned out. All those years he'd given them apparently meant something after all. Score one for Quinn.

A sudden noise brought Josh out of his reverie, and he stiffened, every muscle in his body instantly coiled, ready, his reflexes razor sharp. He listened intently and heard the strange sound again, then moved quickly to the desk to retrieve a gun from the top drawer.

Like a shadow stealing across the room, he made his way down the hall to the open doorway of the master bedroom. His eyes widened in surprise; then he leaned against the doorjamb, shaking his head.

"Hello, Magic Lady," he said dryly. "If you knew how much trouble you've caused me, cat, you wouldn't be in the middle of my bed with that smug expression on your furry face. You are a royal pain."

Magic Lady just purred.

Five

Just after midnight Josh lowered the binoculars and swore under his breath. A little over an hour before, a heavy cloud cover had rolled in, turning the night into an inky wall of darkness. It was as though someone had flicked a switch and turned off the silvery moon and stars, making it impossible to see farther than one's own hand.

The woods, of course, Josh knew, was still out there. But what the two men were doing besides freezing, he didn't know. He had fully expected them to make their move once the deep darkness had provided them with a curtain of safety. But so far—nothing.

There were no lights on in the house, but Josh could see clearly, his eyes having adjusted long ago to the darkness, the furniture appearing as bulky lumps in the silent room. Josh, too, was part of the one-color picture, dressed in black cords and a sweater.

Josh had spent the long evening alternating between slouching in a chair and returning to the window to watch the woods. The black box on the desk was his only link to Kristin beyond seeing the lights of her house down the street. Little noise came from the device. Once, Kristin had sneezed, and Josh had frowned, hoping she hadn't caught a cold during the ridiculous playacting outside her house.

He'd eaten three sandwiches and drunk a quart of milk, then returned to the window. Nothing. And the hours had moved by with agonizing slowness. From the black box had come sounds of cupboards being opened and closed, evidence that Kristin was having dinner. Then, later, she'd lighted a fresh fire. The soft rustle of paper had said that she was reading a book.

And now all was quiet, the lights at Kristin's having gone out an hour before.

Josh sat down again, automatically shifting to accommodate the gun nestled in his belt. He drummed his fingers impatiently on the arm of the chair and frowned. His muscles ached from hours of coiled readiness, his slightly swollen eye throbbed with an annoying, steady tempo, his senses were so heightened that he could feel the hair on his arms rubbing against the material of his sweater.

He was ready to confront the enemy, prepared to win, his body screaming for action. He had been through scenarios like this countless times, knew the nuances of his own body, knew his reflexes were fine-tuned and sharp. Adrenaline pumped into his blood in his anticipation of what was to come, keeping him alert, aware. All of it was familiar.

But tonight one thing was very different.

Kristin.

In the dark room with Joshua the killer was Josh Quinn the man.

And the man was thinking of Kristin.

He didn't like this one little bit. Images of Kristin had no business being in that house with him, yet he had no power to stop them. He felt pulled in two directions at once.

The cold metal of the gun at his back told him he was the killer.

The image of Kristin and the memory of her whispered "I'll be waiting for you, Josh" warmed the man.

He shook his head and ran his hand over the back of his neck, feeling the corded tension. He mentally commanded the men in the woods to make their move. He wanted this over with, damn it, so he could—

Could what? he asked himself. Walk away from Kristin? Never see her again? Never hold or touch or kiss her?

Or— What would it be like, he mused, not to spend the rest of his days alone?

"Forget this," he muttered. The moment was now, and he had a job to do. Where in the hell were those guys? They knew now that Kristin had hurt her ankle, that Josh was the only thing standing between them and the package when it was placed in the mailbox.

Josh retraced his steps, sat down in the chair again and waited.

* * *

Kristin stared up into the darkness in her bedroom, having given up on attempting to sleep. The same question that had been tormenting her for hours still beat painfully against her temples: what was happening to Josh?

Kristin drew in a shaky breath and willed herself to relax. She told herself that Josh would be fine, that there was no reason for her to be so terribly frightened for him. She told herself—and didn't believe a word of it.

She'd had enough of this cloak-and-dagger stuff, she decided. She wasn't cut out for this. She wanted Josh there with her. Right now. He'd say her name in that sexy, rumbly voice of his, take her in his arms, kiss her, hold her and, yes, make love to her.

Anything else? she asked herself dryly. As long as she was ordering her fantasies around, she might as well go for the gusto. Josh Quinn would never leave her. He'd declare his undying love for her, and they'd live happily ever after.

Back up there, madame, she thought. What was this "undying love" business? Why was she fantasizing about a man—a man she didn't love—declaring his love for her? Unless... Oh, merciful heavens, was she in love with Josh? Why didn't she know? Or was she too cowardly to look deep within herself to discover the answer?

Kristin covered her face with her hands and shook her head. She didn't know, nor did she have the mental energy to sort out her feelings. Every thought she had was directed toward worrying about what was happening to Josh at that very moment.

But all she could do was wait.

At 2:17 a.m. they came.

Josh heard the almost inaudible click of the back door lock as it was opened by, he presumed, the same special thin tool he'd used himself many times in the past. He moved out of the chair, drawing his gun from his belt, went to the living room doorway and flattened himself against the wall next to it.

Every muscle was tensed. He was ready.

He waited soundlessly, his breathing controlled.

And they came. The two men were dressed in black. One tall and the other short and stocky, they made their way through the living room, then hesitated. The shorter one gestured toward the hall beyond, which led to the bedrooms.

"Thought you'd never get here," Josh said, his voice ominously low. "Don't move."

The men stiffened, the tall one starting to turn in Josh's direction.

"Try it and you're dead," Josh said. "Drop the guns."

With muttered expletives, the men followed his directive.

"Hands up," Josh said, then reached over to turn on a lamp. He blinked against the sudden glare, then moved forward. He quickly searched each man, finding a knife strapped to the calf of the tall blond one. "Sit, gentlemen," he said, indicating two chairs. "Nice and easy, now."

The men did so, both glowering at Josh, who stood in front of them, his eyes cold.

The blond spoke. "You're a dead man, Quinn."

"Me?" Josh's voice was calm. "I'd say you two are the ones who screwed up. How are you going to explain this to the folks back home—if you ever get there? I'm going to have some real friendly fellas come pick you up."

"You won't get the package," the blond said. "It's ours."

"Wrong," Josh said, his jaw tightening. "You're out of the picture." He kept the gun pointed at the men as he moved toward the desk and the small black box.

The blond's gaze flickered to the coding device, then back to Josh. "You touch that and your lover, Kristin Duquesne, is as good as dead."

Josh stiffened, his eyes narrowed. "You're bluffing. Nice try, but no cigar."

"Why do you think we're so late tonight, Quinn?" the blond taunted him. "We were waiting for more orders. We told our people we had a chance to get the package *and* Joshua Quinn. A man caught in the claws of a willing woman always makes mistakes."

A knot tightened in Josh's stomach, but he didn't let it change the cold expression on his face. "You're crazy, chum. I have the gun, remember? You can quit with the chatter. You're boring me." He reached out toward the box.

"I wouldn't do that, Quinn," a new voice said.

Josh's head snapped up. A man stood in the doorway to the living room, pointing a gun at Josh. The man was huge, taller and more muscular than Josh, and had a scar running down the side of what had once been a handsome face.

"Koltsov," Josh said.

"We meet again, old friend," Koltsov said. "Drop the gun, Quinn."

"And if I don't?"

"Ah, always so brave," Koltsov remarked, moving into the room. "If you don't? Well, to tell you that you will die will only make your patriotic juices flow. No, you won't die. You're worth much more to us alive. It will be your woman who will pay for your foolishness. I have a man waiting for my signal to go inside her house and get her."

"I don't believe you," Josh said. *Kristin!* Damn it, no!

"You had better, my friend," Koltsov said. "I've waited a long time for you to make a mistake." He ran a finger down the jagged white scar on his face. "You owe me for this, and now, at last, you will pay. Oh, yes, we will kill your Kristin Duquesne if you force us to. The great Joshua Quinn has been weakened by a woman. Drop the gun."

Fury burned within Josh. He dropped the gun, his icy black eyes never leaving Koltsov's face.

"Kristin Duquesne knows nothing," Josh said. "You'll pay heavily if you involve a private citizen in this. You've got me—you'll get the package. Leave her alone."

Koltsov laughed. The harsh sound caused Josh to curl his hands into tight fists at his sides.

"Mistakes, mistakes." Koltsov grinned and shook his head. "So it is when you fall in love, Quinn. The best agents in the world have tried to take you out, and it was a woman who brought you to your knees. I thought you knew better.''

A strange noise came from beyond the room, and Josh glanced over to see Magic Lady in the shadows of the hall. Koltsov turned his head in the direction of the sound as the two other men left their chairs to retrieve their guns.

Josh made his move.

He picked up a statue from an end table and flung it at the two agents who were bending over to pick up their guns. In the next instant he lunged toward Koltsov, hitting him full force and smashing him to the ground. Koltsov's gun slid across the carpeting. In a smooth, powerful motion Josh rolled, taking the big man with him and knocking the other two agents to the floor. Vicious epithets in a foreign language filled the air as the four men became a tangle of humanity.

The stocky man groaned as blood poured from a cut on his head where the statue had hit him. Josh pulled his fist back and delivered a stunning blow to Koltsov's jaw. The blond man scrambled for a gun as Josh levered himself up to get to the weapon first.

Josh lost the race.

The blond man grabbed the gun, then turned and fired wildly, panic evident on his face.

Damn it to hell! Josh silently swore as he felt a hot flash of pain rip through his side. Ah, Kristin!

Josh hurled himself forward, his elbow catching the blond man in the stomach and causing him to stagger. But in the next instant the blond regained his footing and slammed the gun down on Josh's head.

Kristin, Josh thought. Kris— Then everything went black.

* * *

At dawn Kristin was up and dressed. Gripping a cup of coffee, she paced the floor, a worried frown on her face.

Something was wrong. Where was Josh? What had happened during the night? Why wasn't Josh at her door, telling her the nightmare was over and that she no longer had reason to be frightened? His absence was screaming at her that something was wrong.

What should she do? she wondered. Josh had told her not to leave the house until he returned. He'd been so sure the men from the woods would come to the Jamesons' during the night. Well, it was morning, and all this was supposed to be over. Josh was supposed to be there with her by now!

Calm down, she told herself. Calm down and wait for Josh.

Josh stifled a moan and struggled against the darkness that threatened to swamp his senses yet again. Through the remaining hours of the night he'd regained consciousness several times, only to be assaulted by blinding pain in his head and side. Despite his efforts he'd fallen back each time into oblivion.

He had to fight against that dark tunnel, he thought groggily, had to determine what the situation was with the foreign agents, with that damn Koltsov. He also had to find out how badly he was hurt. Stay awake, he told himself. Think. Concentrate! Think about Kristin. God, if they touched her, he'd kill them with his bare hands.

No one, Josh vowed as his mind cleared, would harm Kristin. Damn it, she was his!

Pain forced its message into Josh's brain, and he reluctantly acknowledged it. He was on his back on the floor, he realized as he opened his eyes slightly. Light was glaring beneath the drapes, declaring a new day. Kristin must be frantic, wondering where he was, what was happening. Man, did his head hurt. And his side. There was some kind of bandage under his sweater. Koltsov had meant it; they wanted Joshua Quinn alive.

Josh turned his head, wincing against the pain that rocketed through it. His gaze collided with Koltsov's. The man sat in a chair, staring at Josh.

"So," the foreign agent said, "you are awake again. Perhaps this time you will stay with us for more than a few moments. How are you feeling, Quinn?"

"Terrific," Josh said, lifting one hand to his throbbing head.

"You'll live. You have a flesh wound in your side. It is painful, I am sure, but not fatal. You lost a lot of blood. You may have a concussion." Koltsov shrugged. "Who knows? What I do know is that I have the mighty Quinn at last. I have waited a long time for this." He drew a finger down the scar on his face.

"Okay, Koltsov," Josh said, taking a deep, painful breath, "you hold the aces—at the moment. Do you mind if I get up off the floor?"

"Not at all."

Gritting his teeth and holding his side, Josh staggered to his feet, then fell immediately into an easy chair facing Koltsov.

Koltsov clicked his tongue. "You look awful. I doubt that your Kristin Duquesne would be too impressed with you at the moment. Of course, I understand that you two had a bit of a spat yesterday.''

"She hates my guts," Josh said. "I've got this black eye to prove it. You're all wrong about me and Kristin Duquesne, Koltsov. I was stringing her along to get the package. That's it.''

"I think not." Koltsov got to his feet, crossed the room and returned to hand Josh a cup of coffee. "You have fallen hard for the lovely Miss Duquesne.''

Josh took a sip of the strong coffee. "She's not my type.''

"Then it won't matter to you what happens to her.''

Josh's jaw tightened, but he kept silent.

"You give yourself away, my friend. I know you too well. You would gladly tear me limb from limb at the mere mention that harm may come to Miss Duquesne. But you won't have that opportunity. As you said, Quinn, I hold the aces.''

"So?''

"So you are correct in that I would rather not face the ramifications of involving a private citizen in this. Your people do get very hostile about that. They will be upset enough that we have Joshua Quinn, who is going to give us such valuable information. No, I don't wish to harm your Kristin, but it is up to you and how well you cooperate. How badly is her ankle hurt? Can she get to the mailbox?''

"No, she'd never manage the walk to the end of the street.''

"Good. Is she expecting to hear from you today?''

"I doubt it," Josh said. "She's mad as hell at me, remember?''

"Oh, I have my doubts about that. The fury of a woman in love cools very quickly. Telephone her now. Tell her you will bring her mail to her later."

"She's not speaking to me."

"Call her, Quinn."

Josh shrugged and reached for the phone on the end table next to him. Don't blow it, Kristin, he thought. Please don't blow it.

"Wait," Koltsov said. "Press the button on the speaker box I've attached to the phone so I can hear what the lovely lady has to say."

Josh did as instructed, his gaze darting to the listening device on the desk. Kristin's voice would come over that, too, he knew.

"You're slipping in your old age, Koltsov," Josh said. "You don't piece things together as well as you used to. When I call Kristin, you'll hear her voice over this speaker and from that black box on the desk. Men in love don't bug their woman's house. To me Kristin Duquesne is part of an assignment, nothing more."

Koltsov's eyes narrowed as he looked at the black box, then back at Josh. "Call her."

Josh shrugged, the increased pain making him wish that he hadn't, then dialed Kristin's number. She answered on the first ring.

"Yes? Hello?"

"Kristin? Josh. Just listen, okay? I'm sorry about yesterday. I shouldn't have said those things. If you want to go to that Magic Lady person to have your fortune told, that's up to you. I apologize for saying she was a phony. Forgive me?"

Kristin's hand tightened on the receiver until her knuckles turned white. Something was definitely wrong, she thought frantically. Why was Josh talking in riddles, unless—dear heaven, unless someone was listening to everything being said?

"Kristin?"

"Yes, I..." she began, hearing the trembling in her voice. "...I forgive you, Josh. I guess I overreacted. Actually, I really don't think I believe in fortune-tellers."

Beautiful, Kristin, Josh thought. Just hang in there. "Well, that's all behind us now."

"Would you like to come over for breakfast, Josh?"

"Thanks, but I've got to get a couple more hours of sleep. Three friends of mine who knew I was here drove through, and we stayed up half the night playing poker. Two of them are real babes in the woods when it comes to cards."

They were there! Kristin's mind screamed. The two from the woods, and someone else.

"Did you win?" Kristin said, hardly breathing. "At poker?"

"No, not me," Josh said. "I did okay for a while, but that's the way it goes sometimes."

Oh, God. Kristin squeezed her eyes closed for a moment. "Yes, I suppose it does," she managed to say as she pressed her hand to her forehead.

"Kristin," Josh went on, "I don't want you to try to go for the mail with your sore ankle. I'll meet up with the mailman, get both yours and mine, then come by to see you. You stay put and give that ankle a chance to heal."

"Yes, all right. How's your eye?"

"I've got a roaring headache, slugger. Put that together with the muscle I pulled in my side when I carried you into the house, and I feel like I've been in a brawl. I'll live, though."

He was hurt, Kristin thought. His head. His side. Oh, Josh.

"Aren't we a fine pair?" she said. "I'm hobbling around on this ankle like an old lady. I'm going to curl up in front of the fire and not move."

"Good. I'll be over later with your mail. Bye."

"Goodbye, Josh," she said softly.

Kristin replaced the receiver, then pressed her fingertips to her lips, fighting back tears. They had Josh, he was hurt and— No, she wouldn't fall apart. She had to be strong, do whatever Josh needed her to do. She wouldn't let him down. She had to help him. Somehow.

Josh hung up the phone and watched Koltsov cross the room to peer at the black box on the desk.

"Clever," the agent said. "It looks like a piece of junk." He turned to face Josh. "You handled that call rather well. The lovely Miss Duquesne is obviously very devoted to you. I had my share of women, too, before this." He touched his scar. "Perhaps your Kristin wouldn't find you so appealing if you had one of these, Quinn. I will have to give that some thought."

"You do that," Josh said. "It must be obvious to you by now that Kristin knows nothing about the package. There's no reason to involve her."

"We shall see. If the package comes today, we shall all just disappear—you included. Kristin will simply decide you were a real scum."

"And if the package doesn't come today?"

"We shall cross that bridge later, Quinn. She's expecting you to bring her her mail. Let us hope that isn't necessary. You don't look particularly healthy, and it would require my going with you, and I do not wish to be seen. For the sake of your Kristin, I suggest you hope that package arrives today."

"She's not mine," Josh said tightly. "I've been feeding her a bunch of bull."

"Quinn, Quinn," Koltsov said, smiling and shaking his head, "don't take me for a fool. You are finished, victim of the soft body of a woman, instead of the cold blade of a knife. Amazing. Oh, did I tell you about the last ace I hold? I am leaving one of my men behind to watch your Kristin. If you fail to tell us all we want to know, your lovely lady will suffer greatly."

"You bastard," Josh ground out.

Koltsov laughed. "Such intensity for a man who doesn't care. Face it, Quinn. You are in love. You know it, and I know it. Well, so be it. It will work beautifully to my advantage. Now, my friend, on your feet. I shall help you clean up, shave, change clothes, just in case we are to make a social call later. Then we shall get some food in you. You really don't look well at all."

"Go to hell, Koltsov," Josh said, pushing himself slowly to his feet. Koltsov was wrong. Granted, Josh cared for Kristin, cared very much, but he wasn't in love with her. Was he? Oh, hell, forget it. His head hurt. His whole body hurt.

"We are all destined for hell, Quinn," he said. "They reserve places for men like us. Now, let us get you all spruced up."

The morning dragged on.

The ache in Josh's head began to diminish somewhat, but his side was still extremely painful. He'd seen the wound when he'd cleaned up and knew it wasn't serious, but it would definitely restrict his movements. He was weak from loss of blood and in no condition to try to overpower Koltsov and his cronies. Koltsov rebandaged Josh's side; then Josh shaved and dressed in jeans and a sweater. He forced himself to eat a large breakfast, knowing he would need all the strength he could get.

And through it all he thought of Kristin.

She'd been fantastic on the phone, he mused. She was sharp and had picked up immediately on the fact that things had not gone as planned. Only because of her ability to stay calm and play along, she was viewed as an innocent bystander and so was still out of danger. For now.

He'd been in worse spots than this, Josh knew, but he'd always been alone, with only himself to worry about. He'd taken daring chances and won, escaped from situations that had appeared hopeless at the outset.

But this time there was Kristin to consider. Anything he did, he realized, would have a direct effect on her.

Time ticked slowly by.

Just after lunch, the blond man came in the back door and entered the living room.

"Koltsov," he said, "there's a mail truck coming down the road at the end of this street."

Josh started to get to his feet.

"Sit," Koltsov said. He redirected his attention to the blond man. "Go back outside, but keep out of sight. Let me know when he has been to the mailboxes and driven on." The man nodded and left. "So this is it," Koltsov said to Josh. "Maybe. If the package isn't there today, we shall have to readjust our plans."

Josh said nothing.

The blond man came racing back into the house. "The mail truck turned onto this street and is stopped at the woman's house. I couldn't see what he was carrying."

"Damn," Koltsov said. "What game is this, Quinn?"

"I don't know. The report we have is that the package is small, should fit in the mailbox. Kristin may have ordered something, maybe for her artwork, that's too big for the box." Oh, man, he hoped that was all it was. Why in the hell was the mailman going directly to her door?

"Keep watch," Koltsov said to the other agent. The blond disappeared again. Koltsov got to his feet and walked to the desk to stare at the small black box. "Well, thanks to you and your clever device, Quinn, we'll know exactly what is going on over there, won't we? You had better hope, for your woman's sake, that she ordered some very large paintbrushes. No comment, Quinn?"

Josh shot Koltsov an icy look but said nothing. His heart thundered in his chest, and a trickle of sweat ran down his back. He forced himself to appear calm and relaxed, but every muscle in his body was tensed. The pain in his side increased. He riveted his gaze on the black box.

Kristin jumped when the knock sounded at the door. She got slowly to her feet, telling herself she was absolutely, positively not to faint dead away on the floor, then went to answer the summons. Her mouth dropped open when she saw Mr. Grayson, the mailman.

"Hello, Kristin," Mr. Grayson said.

"Hello. This is a surprise. I mean, you don't usually come all the way down to my door to deliver my mail."

"Well, I wanted to ask a favor."

"Yes?"

"My grandson collects stamps, you see. This package I've got for you has some beauties from France...."

No! Kristin's stomach clenched.

"...and I was wondering if you'd save them for him. I'll get them from you later."

"Of course, Mr. Grayson," Kristin said, her knees trembling. "I'll be glad to. I'm not expecting anything from France, though, so maybe you're mistaken about—"

"Nope. See here? It's postmarked Paris. Oh, my grandson will be tickled pink. Thanks, Kristin," he said, handing her the small package. "I'll be talking to you soon."

"Yes," she said, staring at the package. "Soon." She closed the door. Oh, dear God, no! They could hear everything over at the Jamesons'. Oh, Josh. She was so frightened she didn't know what to do. Josh, please!

Josh's hands were curled into tight fists on his thighs, his teeth clenched so tightly that his jaw ached. Kristin's life was teetering on the edge of danger because some kid collected stamps, he thought incredulously. Damn it!

Koltsov turned slowly from the box to face Josh. "So, my friend," he said, "it would appear we are to make a social call on your woman after all."

Six

With shaking hands, Kristin removed the brown wrapping from the small package. As the paper rustled—heard, she knew, through the listening device—she felt as though a hundred enemy eyes were watching her. Her trembling legs threatened to give way, and she moved to the sofa and sat down.

She threw away the brown paper, balancing on her knees the white box she had revealed. Her own movements seemed jerky and uncoordinated to her as her racing heart thudded in her ears. She drew a deep, steadying breath, then slowly lifted the lid from the box. Chewing nervously on her bottom lip, she brushed back the thick layers of tissue paper and peered inside.

"Oh," she gasped. "Oh, my..."

* * *

"She has opened the package," Koltsov said, turning away from the black box. "Let us go, Quinn."

Josh got to his feet, ignoring the hot pain in his side. "Give me a chance to talk to her when we get there, Koltsov. There's no reason to involve her immediately. If she goes along with my story, she'll be none the wiser."

"I don't trust you, Quinn."

"What threat am I to you? You'll be right there, hearing every word I say. If I can get the package from Kristin without her even knowing what it really contains, you'll have avoided the unpleasantness that follows harassing a U.S. citizen. You'll have me and the microdot. You'll be a hero."

Koltsov looked at him for a long moment. "All right," he said, nodding slowly. "I have nothing to lose. I still hold all the aces in this delightful game. You will have your chance to speak first with Miss Duquesne. If there is any hint of a trick, she will pay heavily, and it will be on your conscience." He handed Josh his coat, then put on his own, slipping his gun into a pocket. "I shall leave instructions for my men, and then we shall go. It is time that my men cleared out of here. This is too small a town for so many strange faces to be lingering on one block. I shall send them on ahead to our destination. I can handle things from here on out."

"Bully for you," Josh said sarcastically.

"Do remember, though, Quinn, that I will leave one man behind in the woods to await my orders, should you choose not to cooperate with us."

"I hope he freezes to death," Josh said.

Outside, the air was clear but extremely cold, the sky blue, with not a cloud in sight. Josh walked along beside Koltsov, whose eyes darted continually in all directions. Each step Josh took sent a jarring pain through his side that swept up his back and down his leg. His head throbbed.

His thoughts centered on Kristin.

One more act to go in the play, he mused. One more. If Kristin performed her role as he hoped—prayed—she did, she would remain safe. Could she hang on just a little longer? Or had she reached the end of her rope—in which case she would fling herself at Josh when she saw him and cry with tears of relief that he had come to her at last?

"You still look ragged around the edges, Quinn," Koltsov said, glancing at him. "How will you explain that to your woman?"

Josh shrugged. "I'll say I caught a cold. Or I hardly slept because I knew she was angry with me."

"Ah, how romantic. She will like that. Women enjoy knowing they pull the heartstrings of big, strong men, turning them into marionettes to do their bidding."

"Is that a fact?"

"It is. That is where you made your mistake, Quinn. Women are the same all over the world. Make love to them, yes. But fall in love? Never. You then give them the power to destroy you, just as you have been destroyed. You are a fool, Joshua Quinn. And I will reap the rewards of your foolishness."

"How nice," Josh said dryly. "I'm happy for you, Koltsov. You're a peach of a guy."

Koltsov laughed. "I find American sarcasm amusing." He paused. "So, another few feet and we are there. Remember, Quinn—your woman's safety rests in your hands."

He wouldn't forget, Josh thought. So much, so damn much, depended on what Kristin said and did in the next few minutes. Lord, he hated this. There she'd stand, in the same room with one of the world's most dangerous, ruthless enemy agents, and he had only words with which to protect her.

They stopped on Kristin's porch.

"So, my friend," Koltsov said, "it is up to you. Shall I wish you good luck?"

"Stuff it," Josh said, knocking lightly on Kristin's door. Please, Kristin, he thought. Please don't fall apart now.

The door opened. Josh's heart thundered in his chest.

"Josh!" Kristin said, smiling brightly. "I'm sorry it took me so long to answer, but my ankle slows me down. I'm hopping along like a rabbit. Come in. Oh, this must be one of your poker-playing friends, right? Is he the one who won?"

She was going to do it! Josh felt almost weak with relief. She was playing her part. "Hi, sweetheart," he said, smiling. "Yep, this guy was the big winner, all right."

"Come in, both of you," she said. "I have a lovely fire going." She hopped backward out of their way.

The two men entered the house.

"Kristin," Josh said, "this is Joe Kolter. He works with me. Joe, Kristin Duquesne."

"Mr. Kolter," Kristin said.

"Joe—please," Koltsov said. "This is a lovely home you have . . . Kristin."

"Thank you. Would you two care for some coffee?"

"You should get off that ankle, sweetheart," Josh said, putting his arm around her shoulders. "We don't need any coffee. You come sit down on the sofa."

"Yes, all right. Oh, Josh, the most exciting thing has happened."

"Oh?" he said. He settled her on the sofa, then sat down next to her. Koltsov remained standing, leaning on the mantel.

"Mr. Grayson, the mailman, came right to my door to bring me a package, because he wanted the stamps for his grandson."

"Oh?" Josh said, frowning. What was she up to? All he could do was follow her lead. "What was so special about the stamps?"

Kristin cocked her head to one side. "Darling, do you feel all right? You look rather . . . I don't know, under the weather."

"I'm fine. Go on with your story."

"Well, it's just amazing. Do you remember me telling you that I had an uncle who lived in Paris but who was killed in the war?"

"Yes."

"An old, dear friend of his came across one of my uncle's belongings he'd kept for him, back during the war. The note that was in the package said he finally tracked me down and was sending it to me."

"What did he send you, Kristin?" Josh said, looking directly at her. Damn it, this was it. In another few seconds Koltsov would have the microdot, and there was nothing Josh could do to stop it. Kristin must think she was assuring his safety by handing it over. He'd never felt so helpless in his life.

Kristin picked up the white box, brushed back the tissue and lifted out a small object. Josh stiffened. Koltsov pushed himself away from the mantel and came closer to the sofa.

"A thimble," Josh said.

"Oh, Josh," Kristin said, "not just a thimble. This is made of wafer-thin bone china. It was handmade in France. See the seal? Look at the bird sitting on the flowered branch. Isn't it exquisite?"

Josh glanced quickly at Koltsov, then back at the thimble. "Yeah, it's very pretty. I wouldn't be surprised if it was worth a lot of money."

"I would say so," Koltsov said.

"Oh, I would never sell it," Kristin said, nestling the thimble back in the tissue. "It belonged to my uncle, so it's an heirloom of sorts."

"No, no, I'm not suggesting that you sell it," Josh said quickly. "Listen, Joe came through here with the hope that I could help him with a computer problem he's on a deadline to fix. The printouts aren't giving me the information I need, so I'm going to have to fly to New York with him for a couple of days."

"Oh, dear," Kristin said.

"We'll be taking my car to the nearest airport. Anyway," Josh went on, "I could take the thimble with me and have it appraised for you so you can get the proper insurance on it. Maybe I can find you a nice little glass case to keep it in, too."

"Well..." Kristin said slowly.

"That sounds like a good idea," Koltsov said.

"Yes, all right," Kristin said. "Oh, Josh, I wish you weren't leaving."

"I won't be gone long. Listen, call Jeff Jameson, will you? Tell him the hot water heater is on the blink at the house and ask him if he wants me to have it fixed while his folks are away."

"I had hot water for my shower," Koltsov said.

"Well, I didn't," Josh said. "Something is wrong with the thing." He got up and walked to the desk. "There. I've written down Jeff's number. There's no big rush to have it done. The other guys left, and Joe and I are leaving now. If Jeff wants me to tend to it, I'll do it when I get back."

"All right," Kristin said, nodding. "I'll call him."

"Good," Josh said to Kristin. "We've got to get on the road. I'll be back as soon as I can. I'll take very good care of your thimble." He moved back to stand in front of her.

"And of yourself?" she said softly, looking directly into his dark eyes.

"Sure. You . . . stay off of that ankle."

Their eyes held for a long moment, a painful, heartrending moment in which they didn't dare say what they yearned to say.

Koltsov cleared his throat. "We must go, Quinn."

Josh leaned down and brushed his lips over Kristin's. "See you soon."

"Yes," she whispered, fighting back tears.

Josh put the lid on the box and straightened. "Oh," he said, reaching into his pocket. "Keep this for me." He handed her his lighter. Kristin's eyes widened. "I'm going to quit smoking. I won't . . . I won't be needing that anymore."

Oh, dear Lord, no! She curled her fingers around it. She knew how much that lighter meant to him. He was telling her that his life was in danger.

"I'll keep the lighter safe, Josh," she said, hoping her voice was steady. "You might change your mind about needing it."

"You never know..." he said. "Don't come to the door. We'll see ourselves out."

"Goodbye," Koltsov said. He glanced at the paper on the desk on his way to the door.

"Yes, goodbye," Kristin said, watching as the two men started to leave. "Josh?"

He stopped and looked at her. "Yes?"

"I'll be waiting for you," she said, a soft sob catching in her throat.

He took a step toward her. "Kristin, I—"

"Quinn," Koltsov said, grabbing Josh's arm, "we have to go."

"Yeah," Josh said, looking at Kristin for another moment. "Yeah, okay."

The men left the house and closed the door behind them.

Kristin cried.

She hugged the gold lighter to her breast and sobbed. Then, moments later, as quickly as she had started, she stopped, her mind racing as she wiped the tears from her cheeks.

She was to call Jeff Jameson, she thought. Josh had told her to, and he'd made it clear that no one would be in the house to hear her through the listening devices. Jeff Jameson was a government agent? Jeff taught high school English and... Oh, how did she know who was or wasn't a government agent?

But she herself had better start thinking like one, because Josh's life depended on it. Calm down, she told herself, taking a deep breath. She had to be positive that Josh and Joe Kolter, or whatever his real name was, didn't go back into the Jamesons' house, where they would be able to hear her make the call.

Kristin ran down the hall to her bedroom and peered through the curtains. Josh and the man were still on their way to the Jamesons'. Josh was clutching his side and— Oh, dear heaven, how badly was he hurt?

Outside, Josh stopped walking as he was assaulted by a wave of dizziness.

"Move!" Koltsov snapped. "What game are you playing, Quinn?"

"Game, hell," Josh grated. "You try tromping along with a bullet wound, Koltsov."

"Yes, yes, well, let's go." Koltsov looked at the white box he'd taken from Josh the moment they'd left Kristin's house. "I have precious cargo here to deliver. Come, Quinn—enough is enough."

Josh gritted his teeth against the pain as Kristin's tear-choked voice echoed in his ears. *I'll be waiting for you, Josh.*

"Quinn!"

"Yeah, I'm coming. I saved your butt back there at Kristin's, you know, Koltsov."

"Oh?"

"I charmed Kristin into giving me that thimble. You probably would have lost patience and grabbed it out of her hands. Then you'd be in trouble up to your neck. You're such a fool."

"Fool!" Koltsov yelled. "Whom do you call a fool?"

"You, my friend." Josh snorted in disgust. "I've been one step ahead of you for years, Koltsov. Oh, you're good, but I'm better, always have been."

Koltsov's scarred faced contorted in anger. "Not this time, Quinn. I am the winner. Word will spread. Everyone will know that it was Koltsov who brought down Joshua Quinn. I will be held in high esteem. I also have the package. You have lost, Quinn."

Josh walked slowly past him. "Have I?" he said, his voice low, his eyes cold. Perfect, he thought. Koltsov was losing control of his temper. He'd seen the creep in action before, had seen him lose his edge because his volatile temper got in the way. Slowly but surely Josh was shifting the aces to his own hand.

At the Jamesons' Josh saw his suitcase on the ground next to his car in the driveway. Thank God, he thought. There was no reason to go back inside the house, where Koltsov could hear Kristin making the phone call. He'd been taking a risk in telling her to dial the number he'd left her, but it had been his only chance.

"Quinn, get in the car," Koltsov said. "You will drive."

"I'm not sure I can," Josh said, holding his injured side.

"You shall drive!" Koltsov roared.

Josh shrugged. "Whatever. Where are we going?"

"To the coast. A boat waits for us. I have planned this to perfection."

"I'm impressed," Josh said dryly.

Minutes later, Josh drove slowly away from the Jamesons' with Koltsov in the passenger seat. The white box was next to the enemy agent, who gripped his gun where it rested on his thigh.

"Do not speed," Koltsov said. "Do nothing to draw attention to us." He sighed and shook his head. "The puppets are driving ahead to the boat. Why do they give me such inferior men to work with?"

"Yep," Josh said. "Tough to get good help these days."

They passed Kristin's house. Somehow I'll be back, Kristin. Wait for me.

"Damn it, Quinn," Koltsov said, bringing Josh back from his thoughts. "When I said don't speed, I did not mean crawl along like a snail."

"Got it," Josh said, pressing the gas pedal. Quit thinking about Kristin, he told himself. He had to watch for a chance to make his move. And he had to do it before Koltsov cooled off, dampened down that temper and got himself under control again.

The pain in Josh's side was getting worse, and he could only guess that the damn wound was becoming infected. With the increased pain came an unnatural heat to his skin, which meant he was starting to run a fever. Not good. His reflexes, his thinking processes—everything would be slowed down. He had to act. Soon.

Kristin watched the car as Josh and the other man drove away from the Jamesons'. Tears misted her vision, but she blinked them away, then ran back into the living room to snatch up the piece of paper from the desk. She dialed the number, not relinquishing her hold on the precious gold lighter. She heard a crackling noise on the line, a hum and more static. Then a man's voice came over the line.

"Yes?"

"May I speak to... Jeff Jameson, please?" Kristin said.

"Who's calling?"

"Kristin Duquesne."

There was a moment of silence. "Where did you get this number, Miss Duquesne?"

"From Josh Quinn," she said, knowing her voice was trembling. "Is Jeff there?"

"No, Jeff would have no reason to be here. I'm Chet Bell. What's going on?"

Kristin's legs refused to support her for another second, and she sat down on the chair at the desk.

"Mr. Bell," she said, taking a deep breath, "listen to me carefully. Josh's life is in danger. He just left here with an enemy agent he called Joe Kolter. The man is bigger than Josh, heavier, and has a scar down one side of his face."

"Holy hell," Chet said. "Koltsov."

"There are other agents, too," Kristin said, "who were in the woods. They've already gone."

"We know about those two. They're small potatoes. But Koltsov is—Miss Duquesne, I know that Quinn told you everything that's taking place. If Koltsov stays true to form, he's left someone behind in case Quinn doesn't cooperate and... We'll take care of that situation, but in the meantime do nothing to draw attention to yourself. I assume that Koltsov has the package."

"Yes, and he also has Josh."

"What makes you so sure that Quinn's life is in danger? Koltsov is good, but Quinn is better, always has been. That scar on Koltsov's face is proof of that."

"Josh has already been hurt—his head, his side. He looks terrible," Kristin said, her voice quavering as tears welled up in her eyes. "He—he gave me his gold lighter. He said he wouldn't be needing it anymore."

Chet Bell was silent for a long moment. "I see," he finally said quietly.

Kristin lifted her chin. "Is that proof enough for you?"

"More than enough. All right, Miss Duquesne, tell me everything you know, every word, no matter how trivial, that was spoken while Koltsov was there with Quinn. I need to know if they left in a vehicle, what it looked like, who was driving, what they were wearing. Take your time. Think carefully. I'm turning on a recording machine that will take down everything you say."

"All right."

"Be sure of your details, Miss Duquesne. If Quinn gave you that lighter... Well, go ahead. Are you ready?"

"Yes," Kristin said, pressing her hand to her forehead. Her mind, her heart, her soul centered on one image, one purpose.

Josh...

Josh and Koltsov drove in silence, passing through several small towns, then coming to a narrow, twisting dirt road that was covered with deep chuckholes. Josh slowed the vehicle as he maneuvered around the worst of the holes. Koltsov shifted impatiently in his seat.

Then, in the distance, Josh saw his chance. A huge tree grew close to the edge of the road, its branches stark and bare. It was risky as hell, he mused. But it was all he had. If he got on Koltsov's boat, his chances of escape would be somewhere between slim and none.

He allowed himself one fleeting image of Kristin, then focused on the tree ahead, gauging the distance.

Easy, he told himself. A few more seconds... wait...almost, almost... Now!

Josh stamped on the gas pedal, and the car shot forward.

"What are you—" Koltsov began to say, but he never finished.

With the sickening noises of breaking glass and twisting metal, the car slammed into the tree.

And then all was quiet.

Seven

Just after dawn the next morning, Kristin stood on her front porch, staring up at the cloudless pale blue sky. She huddled deeper into her red parka, pushing her hands farther into her pockets to ward off the chill wind.

She'd limped out onto the porch, not knowing whether or not there was still a man watching her from the woods. She saw no movement in the trees or in any of the other houses on the street, and she had the irrational thought that she was the only living soul left on the face of the earth.

She had stayed close to the telephone after talking to Chet Bell. She'd been waiting, praying, for word that Josh was safe and out of the hands of the enemy agents. But the hours had dragged by in silence, on into the night.

She hadn't been able to sit there a moment longer. She'd grabbed her coat and fled to the porch for a brief escape from the walls of the house, which seemed to be closing in around her. She'd left the front door ajar so that she could hear the telephone.

As Kristin filled her lungs with the biting-cold air, the lingering cobwebs were swept from her brain.

Where was Josh? she wondered for the thousandth time. Chet Bell had assured her he'd telephone with any news, but so far—nothing. Only silence—the most frightening silence she had ever heard.

Kristin closed her eyes and gathered her memories of Joshua Quinn. A soft smile touched her lips as she curled her fingers more tightly around the gold lighter in her pocket. Josh, she thought as his image flitted before her.

What had happened after she'd spoken with Chet Bell?

And what of the future? Was she in love with Josh? What were his feelings for her? No, until she knew Josh was safe she wouldn't dwell on anything beyond the present.

The sound of a car brought Kristin instantly alert, and she stiffened as she saw a black sedan pull into her driveway. A man got out, walked across the yard and came up onto the porch.

"Hello, Miss Duquesne," he said, nodding. "I'm Chet Bell."

Tightening her hold on the lighter, Kristin glanced at the woods, then back at the man in front of her.

"Oh?" she said. "How can I be sure of that? Do you have identification?"

He took a small flat case from his pocket and flipped it open for her inspection. Kristin looked at it, then at his boyish face and his wild thatch of red hair.

"I know, I know," he said, his grin making him appear even younger, "I don't look like a government agent." He shrugged. "What can I say? I'm for real." His smile faded. "We've taken care of your watchdog in the woods, by the way."

"That's comforting. Mr. Bell—"

"Chet."

"Chet, where is Josh? You said you'd call me and tell me what happened. Why are you here? Is Josh—"

"Whoa," he said, raising his hand. "Could we go inside? I'm freezing out here."

"Yes, of course. Josh hates the cold, too. He—I'm sorry. I'm starting to babble again. It's just that I've been so worried about Josh." She spun around and went into the house. Chet Bell followed her.

Once inside, they removed their coats. Then Kristin turned to the agent.

"Would you like some coffee?" she asked.

"Yes, please, sounds great. You get the coffee and I'll remove the listening devices from in here."

"You know where they are? You've talked to Josh?"

"Get the coffee, okay?"

Kristin resisted the urge to demand that he tell her—now—everything about Josh. She went into the kitchen and prepared a tray of coffee, cream and sugar. Agents told a person things when they were good and ready. She was rapidly running out of patience, however.

Back in the living room, she motioned for Chet to sit on the sofa. He slipped those listening devices into his pocket and went into the kitchen for the rest, then returned and settled on the sofa. Kristin perched on the opposite end and looked at him.

He took a deep swallow of coffee, then met her gaze. "Miss Duquesne—"

"Kristin."

"Kristin, I'm going to have to ask you to pack a suitcase with enough clothes for a few days and accompany me to Washington."

Kristin's eyes widened. "Why?"

"It's necessary."

"What kind of an answer is that?" she asked, frowning.

Chet smiled. "A typical government answer."

"Well, I'm not budging until you tell me how Josh is."

"He's going to be fine."

"*Going* to be fine?"

"You'll get a full report when we get to Washington."

"No," she said, folding her arms across her chest. "You'll tell me now."

Chet sighed. "I was afraid of that. Quinn is in the hospital—"

"Hospital?" she nearly shrieked.

"He's going to be all right. I swear it. The bullet wound on his side became infected. They're treating it with antibiotics. He's pretty battered from the car wreck, but there are no broken bones.''

"Car wreck?'' she whispered.

Chet smiled. "It was a beauty of a move, a typical Josh Quinn first-class act. He smashed that car right into a tree. Koltsov has a broken leg and is nicely under wraps. We got the agents on the boat, too.''

"And the, um, package?''

"I wasn't told what happened to it. I assume our people got it when they picked up Quinn and Koltsov. Anyway, Quinn is a bit of a mess at the moment—and in a really rotten mood—but he's going to be fine.''

"And you're taking me to him?''

"Not…exactly. There are some people who would like to speak with you in Washington. All I was told was to give you a brief medical report on Quinn and what had happened after he left here with Koltsov, then bring you in.''

"Josh didn't ask to see me?'' Kristin said softly.

"Oh, well, I don't know about that. They said he was ranting and raving about being kept in the hospital. The guy is sick as a dog, beat up from head to toe, and he's ready to take people apart. I haven't seen him myself.''

"Why were you sent to get me? Who wants to see me, if not Josh?''

"I really don't know anything beyond my orders to bring you back to Washington. The sooner we get there, the quicker you'll have your answers. Go pack. Just bring slacks and sweaters like you're wearing, okay?''

"I guess so," she said, getting to her feet. "I won't be long."

While Kristin packed, her mind raced, digesting what Chet had said. Josh was going to be all right, and for that she was grateful. He'd smashed the car into a tree? she marveled. Had that been a dumb thing to do? No, Chet Bell had certainly been impressed with Josh Quinn's innovative solution to the dilemma. The enemy agents had all been caught, and it was over.

Over? Everything? What she and Josh had shared, what they might have in the future, was over? No, she had to calm down, quit jumping to conclusions.

But oh, God, she thought frantically, it hadn't all been an act on his part, had it? The kisses, the tender words he had spoken about the wondrous things that had been taking place between them? That had been for real, hadn't it? Or had it all been in the line of duty, a virtuoso performance?

Kristin sat on the edge of the bed and pressed her hands to her flushed cheeks. Stop it, she told herself. She was on her way to Washington, where Josh was. They'd let her see him, wouldn't they? They'd better, or she'd make Josh's ranting and raving seem civilized compared to the fit she'd pitch.

With a sigh she got to her feet. Suddenly feeling exhausted, she picked up her suitcase and walked slowly from the room.

Hours later, Kristin stood staring out the window of her hotel room at the skyline of Washington, D.C. It was very impressive, she supposed, but at the moment she didn't care. Her suite, which had a separate living room, was ritzy, but she didn't care. Flying in a private jet with Chet Bell had been a new experience, but she didn't care.

She wanted to see Joshua!

A knock sounded at the door. She hurried to answer, first looking through the peephole as Chet had instructed her to do. She saw Chet's boyish face and that of a stern-looking man who stood next to him. She opened the door.

"Hi, Kristin," Chet said as he came into the room. The other man followed.

"Hello," she said.

"Kristin," Chet said, "I'd like you to meet Mr. Jones, my boss."

"And Josh's boss?" she said, closing the door. Jones? These people certainly didn't have much imagination. "How do you do, Mr. Jones?"

"Kristin," he said, extending his hand. She shook it. "May we sit down?"

"Of course," she said, gesturing toward a grouping of chairs. "I'm afraid I don't have anything to offer you." The three sat. "Are you Josh's boss, Mr.... Jones?"

"In a manner of speaking," he said. "I'm in charge of the investigation at this point."

"Investigation?" Kristin said.

"There was," Mr. Jones explained, "a breach of security with regard to this assignment. Quinn was not authorized to tell you what was taking place. It was decided that we would go along with his judgment in the matter in the hope that his instinct to trust you was sound. That's why you're here, Kristin. We need to gather our facts, put all the pieces together.''

"I don't think I understand," Kristin said slowly.

"Kristin, the microdot was not found at the scene of Quinn's accident."

Kristin looked at Mr. Jones steadily but said nothing.

"I've gone over this countless times with Quinn," Mr. Jones said. "I hated to hammer at him, with him in that physical condition, but I had no choice. National security is at risk here. Correct me if I'm wrong, but it seems you had the thimble in your possession, with no one else in attendance, from the time you opened the package until Quinn and Koltsov arrived at your house. Is that right?"

"Did Josh tell you that?" Kristin asked.

"Is the information correct, Kristin?"

"Yes, but . . . Mr. Jones, did he urge you to zero in on the time I had the package to myself? Was it Josh Quinn who feels that I have to account for my actions?"

"I'm not at liberty to say," Mr. Jones said. "Why don't you tell me exactly what you did from when you opened the package until the time Quinn and Koltsov got to your house?"

Kristin was silent.

"Kristin," Chet interjected. "Mr. Jones is a very important man. Maybe I didn't make that clear."

"Important to you, Chet, but he isn't my boss. I'm not saying a word to anyone until I've seen Josh."

Mr. Jones leaned forward in his chair. "Kristin, I'm a high-ranking official of this government. You must answer my questions."

"I will, once I've seen Josh," she said. Oh, mercy, she was so frightened she could hardly breathe. This was a nightmare, and she didn't know what to do. She had to see Josh!

Mr. Jones sat back in his chair and stared at Kristin through narrowed eyes. She met his gaze straight on. The seconds ticked by.

"All right," Mr. Jones said.

"You're kidding," Chet said. "I mean, yes, sir."

"Perhaps it's better this way," Mr. Jones said. "Quinn's career could be at stake here. We'll drive to the hospital and conduct the questioning in his presence. Medically speaking, I don't think he should be up to more of this, but the hollering he's been doing about everything indicates he is. Let's go." After this, Mr. Jones seemed to be talking to himself, rather than addressing Kristin or Chet. "I want you both to know that I sure didn't ask to head this investigation. Josh Quinn has given years of dedicated service to this country, and they're landing on him with both feet because this assignment was screwed up and Quinn stepped out of his range of authority. There have got to be some plausible answers to all of this."

"Mr. Jones," Kristin said, "the answers are very clear. Joshua Quinn no longer trusts me." She swallowed past the ache in her throat. "Obviously I'm here in Washington to be interrogated because of that distrust."

"Take it easy, Kristin," Chet said. "They're just starting to gather the facts."

"Gather what facts you wish," she said, getting to her feet, her voice trembling. "I have all of mine. I understand exactly what Mr. Quinn is thinking."

"Don't make any assumptions, Kristin," Mr. Jones said. "Shall we go?"

"What's your real name?" Kristin said, planting her hands on her hips.

Mr. Jones pulled out a flat leather case and flipped it open for Kristin's inspection.

"Oh," she said weakly. "Fred Jones. I'll be darned. I'll, um, get my coat and purse."

The hospital had the smells that usually went along with an institution of its kind, as well as the people who spoke in hushed tones.

Kristin had said nothing during the drive from the hotel, nor did she remember much of the ride through the heavy traffic. She was wrapped in a cocoon of misery, the realization of why she was there beating against her mind—and her heart. Fred Jones's refusal to assure her it wasn't Josh who'd questioned her motives screamed the message that Josh didn't trust her.

Trust, Kristin thought bitterly. She'd trusted Joshua after so many years of trusting no man. He'd stridden boldly into her home and then, inch by emotional inch, won her mind, her heart, her very soul.

Was she in love with a man who didn't trust her? She didn't want to know the answer, couldn't bear the thought of discovering her true feelings for Josh. And what about Josh? What they had shared, what she had believed had been blossoming between them, was being tossed aside as he put her through this frightening experience in order to perform his role as a government agent. A role, she now feared, he had never stopped performing, not even when he'd held her in his arms.

Kristin stepped into the elevator, Chet and Fred Jones on either side of her. She felt like a prisoner being led to her execution. She admitted that she wanted to see Josh to assure herself that he really was going to be all right. But she didn't want to talk to him, didn't want to hear the words that would fling his distrust against her like physical blows.

The elevator stopped, and the three stepped out. Chet indicated that they were to go to the left, and Kristin marched along, her stomach doing strange flip-flops.

She would not cry, she told herself firmly, no matter what took place in that room with Josh.

As the trio turned a corner, two men who were leaning casually against the wall, chatting, suddenly came to attention.

"Oh, good night," Kristin mumbled. "More of you guys?"

Chet chuckled.

"Mr. Jones," one of the men said with a nod.

"Bill," Mr. Jones said. "Everything quiet here?"

"Yes, sir. Well, sort of. Mr. Quinn isn't very happy about being here, as you know."

Before Fred Jones could reply, the door opened and a plump gray-haired nurse came out.

"Hello, Martha," Fred said. "How's our boy?"

Martha smiled. "Fred, you do bring me some real dillies to tend to. That handsome devil in there is the worst of the lot. The nurses are going to draw numbers from a fishbowl to see who gets to murder him."

Fred laughed. "That bad, huh?"

"Oh, he's something," Martha said, still smiling, "but I'll keep him in line. He's dealing with Martha O'Toole now."

"He's met his match," Fred said. "We're going to go in and talk to him for a bit."

"Well," Martha said, "I can't stop you, but he does need his rest—not that he's resting. He's just fussing. Don't be surprised if he falls asleep in the middle of a sentence. He's exhausted, but he won't give in to it. Personally, Fred, I'd say that once his fever is under control, he'd recuperate better somewhere else. He's keeping himself in a real dither, when what he needs is peace and quiet. He is a handsome so-and-so, I must say, bruises and all.... Well, call me if you need me."

"Thanks, Martha," Fred said. She nodded and hurried away. "We're not to be disturbed," he told the two men outside the room. "No matter how loud it gets." He turned to Kristin. "Ready?"

"I guess so," she said quietly. Chet patted her shoulder in a comforting gesture.

Gripping her purse in front of her to keep her trembling under control, Kristin lifted her chin and followed Fred Jones into the room, Chet bringing up the rear.

And then she saw him.

In no more than one beat of Kristin's wildly thudding heart she took in every detail of him. His thick dark hair was tousled, as if he'd raked his fingers through it. She noticed a scrape on his cheekbone, in addition to the slight discoloration where she'd punched him in the eye. He sat propped up against the stark white pillows, the sheet pulled up to his waist. His bare torso was wrapped in white bandages, and numerous bruises and scrapes marred the perfection of his chest, shoulders and arms. He looked so terribly tired, Kristin thought.

And his eyes—his eyes were dark and stormy. His brows were knit in a frown, and his jaw was clenched in anger.

To Kristin, Josh Quinn was absolutely beautiful.

"Hello, Josh," she said softly.

Josh's gaze flickered over her, and she thought, though she wasn't sure, that for a brief second she saw a warm glow in the depths of his eyes before he looked coldly at Fred Jones.

"Damn it, Fred, I've told you over and over that— Ah, hell," Josh said. "Ask your questions. Let's get this nightmare finished."

She wouldn't cry, Kristin told herself, blinking back her tears. Oh, dear God, he hadn't even acknowledged her. All he knew was that he wanted this—her— finished.

"Shall we sit down?" Fred said calmly.

Josh reached for a pack of cigarettes and a book of matches on the bedside table. Kristin opened her purse, took out the gold lighter and walked to the edge of the bed. Unable to speak, she held it out to him. He took it from her, and their eyes met.

Oh, Josh, Kristin silently pleaded, why?

Ah, Kristin, Josh thought. His beautiful Kristin. His warm and wonderful Kristin.

His eyes changed from black ice to tender dark pools.

"Josh?" she whispered.

"Kristin, I—" he began. Then he stopped, but his gaze never left hers.

That unknown emotion swirling within him became crystal clear at last.

Love.

He was in love with Kristin Duquesne.

He let the word drift through his mind and his heart, then allowed it to settle, slowly, slowly, in the place he'd guarded so carefully: his soul.

And he was filled with the greatest joy, the greatest peace and the greatest warmth that he'd ever known.

"Let's sit down," Fred said, his voice firm.

The moment was lost, but Josh knew that for him it was a moment he would never forget. He glared at Fred as Kristin sat down in a chair next to the bed.

"Quinn," Fred said, "I realize you're not feeling up to par, but an official report has to be filed. You're aware that a serious breach of security took place when you informed Kristin, without authorization, of the details of what was taking place. If things had gone as planned, we would have let it go, but obviously they didn't. So let's start with that. Why, Quinn? Why did you tell her?"

Because she was frightened out of her mind, you idiot, Josh raged. Because he probably had already fallen in love with her but hadn't recognized it. And none of this was any of the government's business!

"Quinn?" Fred said.

"Just write it up, Fred," Josh said wearily. "It was a blatant breach of security, pure and simple. Turn it in in triplicate. I blew it, okay? The whole damn thing. They'll hand me my walking papers, and that'll be that."

"No, damn it," Fred said. "Give me something to defend you with, Quinn. You've done too much, for too many years, for this country to end it this way."

"Just give it a rest!" Josh yelled. "I've got nothing else to say. Yeah, you've got Koltsov. Big deal. It was my assignment for months, and the bottom line is I came up empty-handed, as well as overstepping my authority. Involving Kristin was a giant mistake on my part."

"How dare you," she whispered, getting slowly to her feet. "How dare you call me a mistake, Mr. Quinn."

Josh's eyes widened in surprise.

"If you weren't so battered up I'd punched you in the other eye," she went on, her voice rising. "Yes, you told me what was happening. Call it a breach of security if you want, but I see it as a human gesture."

"Kristin, I—" Josh started to say.

"Shut up, Quinn," she said. "You swore to me that what we shared was real, had nothing to do with what was beyond our door. I did my part to help you accomplish what you needed to do, but for what? To find out that it was all an act to you and I'm nothing more than a mistake?'' She took a deep breath, fighting her tears. ''A mistake so embarrassing to you that you won't even defend yourself to save your career. Well, I'm going to defend it for you. I trusted you, Josh, but now your distrust of me has destroyed it, destroyed everything. But no matter what you believe me to be, I can prove to these people that you did not make a mistake. And then, for all I care, you can take a flying leap!''

''Kristin,'' Josh said. ''Please, I—''

''Just shut up!'' she said, tears spilling onto her cheeks. She opened her purse with shaking hands, pulled out a wad of tissue paper and dropped it on the bed. ''That's the thimble my uncle sent. There was one exactly like it in my mother's belongings. I switched them before I gave you the package. The microdot was never out of my possession. I kept it safe while—'' she choked on a sob ''—while I waited for you, Joshua Quinn.''

''Oh, God, Kristin,'' Josh said, reaching for her.

''Don't touch me,'' she said, backing away. She turned to look at Fred Jones. ''So you see, Mr. Jones,'' she quavered, ''the assignment was a success. The microdot was never close to being in enemy hands. Josh involved a private citizen out of brilliance, not as part of a mistake that should cost him his career. You have no cause for complaint against Mr. Quinn. If you'll excuse me now, I'll wait for you in the hall.'' She strode across the room.

''Kristin, wait!'' Josh yelled.

She stopped at the door and turned to look at him, heedless of the tears streaming down her face.

"No, Josh," she said, her voice hardly more than a whisper, "I can't wait, not knowing that you feel I was a mistake, that it was all part of a role you were playing. Goodbye, Josh."

"Damn it, Kristin," he bellowed, "come back here!"

Kristin hurried from the room, wanting only to run as fast and as far as she could. She had to escape from the shattering pain that was consuming her, from the chilling knowledge that once again she'd trusted the wrong man. Tears blurred her vision, and she bumped into one of the big men by the door.

"I'm sorry, ma'am," the man said, "but I'll have to ask you to stay here until Mr. Jones gives you clearance to leave."

"Fine," Kristin said. She crossed the hall and leaned against the wall, wrapping her hands around her elbows. She willed herself not to cry, but tears slid steadily down her cheeks and along her throat.

She felt so empty, she thought, and so very, very cold.

In Josh's room, Fred Jones pressed his hand flat on Josh's chest. "For the last time, Quinn," Fred said, "you're not getting out of this bed."

"I have to go after her," Josh said. "Damn it, Fred, she thinks I didn't trust her. Why did you pick her up and bring her in as though she were suspected of treason? I'd made it clear that Kristin wasn't guilty of anything."

"I had my orders, Quinn," Fred said. "I couldn't tell her you were furious that she was under suspicion. The powers that be wanted first reactions to surface. Real emotions. They didn't want Kristin to think she had an ally in you."

Josh mumbled an expletive.

"Well, you got real emotions, all right," Chet said, coming to the edge of the bed. He shook his head. "That is one very upset lady out there in the hall." He looked at Fred's hand, which was still pressed to Josh's chest. "Want me to sit on him, Mr. Jones? I wouldn't normally volunteer for a suicide mission, but in his present condition I figure I can handle him."

"Cute," Josh said sullenly.

"Quinn," Fred said, lifting his hand, "you know my report will clear both you and Kristin, but I feel very bad about what happened here. How can I help? What do you want me to do? I could tell Kristin that she misinterpreted the facts."

Leaning back on the pillows with a weary sigh, Josh closed his eyes.

"No," he said. "I want your word that you won't do that, Fred. This is between Kristin and me."

"Do you want me to bring her back in here?" Fred asked.

"No," Josh said, opening his eyes. "She's too upset. I'll just have to wait until I can get out of this place, then go to her myself. In the meantime, don't explain things to her. It's up to me to set it to rights. Though how I'm going to do that, I have no idea."

"When in doubt," Chet said cheerfully, "cheat."

Josh lifted his head and narrowed his eyes. "Desperate men do desperate things. Speak, Chet, and this had better be good."

Chet grinned. "Piece of cake."

It seemed like an eternity to Kristin before Fred Jones and Chet came out of Josh's room. She glanced at them, then averted her eyes, not wanting them to see her tear-stained face.

Fred crossed the hall to stand in front of her, the thimble in his hand. "Your government thanks you for this."

"Oh, you're welcome," she said, waving a hand breezily in the air.

"I'm sorry you're so upset," Fred said. "I wish…"

Chet cleared his throat and joined them. "Mr. Jones wishes that he could say it's all over, but that isn't quite true."

"What?" Kristin said, wiping her hands over her cheeks. "Why not?"

"Official procedure," Chet said. "The government is really into official procedure, right, Mr. Jones? Yep. You see, Mr. Jones has to write a report—in triplicate, of course—then present it to a board of inquiry. They'll go over it with a fine-tooth comb, line by line. It's slow going—that's for sure."

"It's also ridiculous," Kristin said.

"No, it's official procedure," Chet said pleasantly. "Anyway, things won't be wrapped up until the board has ruled." He paused. "I suppose you could go home in the meantime, but—"

"But," Kristin interrupted, "I'll bet that the next thing you're going to say is that one of you spy types would be coming along to keep an eye on me."

"Bingo," Chet said, smiling.

"Oh, for heaven's sake," she said, "you can't be serious."

"'Fraid so," Chet said. "Official procedure, you know. Thing is, we have this little problem."

Fred Jones made a strange choking noise.

"Problem?" Kristin repeated, leaning slightly toward him. "Which is?"

"We're a tad short of men at the moment, due to the fact that there are a lot of busy bad guys out there right now..."

Fred Jones muttered something.

"...and," Chet went on, "there are two of you and only one of me."

"You've lost me," Kristin said, shaking her head.

"I've been assigned to watch you," Chet said, rocking back and forth on the balls of his feet. "You—and Quinn. Two of you. One of me."

Kristin squinted at him. "I don't like the sound of this."

"I didn't think you would," Fred said.

"Yeah, it's rough," Chet said. "You and Quinn aren't exactly getting along. But—" he shrugged "—those are the breaks. I'll be there to play referee. You can stay at opposite ends of your house or something."

"You're bringing Josh to my house?" Kristin yelled.

"Hush," a passing nurse said. "This is a hospital."

"Or we can all stay in your hotel room here," Chet said. "Whichever you prefer. We aim to please."

"I'm going home," Kristin said firmly.

"Okeydokey," Chet said. "We'll leave just as soon as the hospital releases Quinn."

"Mr. Jones," Kristin said, "this can't be legal. It's absurd."

"Official procedure," Fred said, staring at his shoes.

Kristin brushed past them and marched down the hall. "My congressman is going to hear about this. Forget that—I'm writing to the president."

Fred Jones rolled his eyes.

Chet Bell looked extremely pleased with himself.

Eight

————

For the next three days Chet kept Kristin so busy she hardly had time to think. He gave her a complete tour of Washington, and Kristin was enthralled by the nation's capital. To her own amazement she fell asleep quickly each night, instead of tossing and turning and thinking of Josh.

It was as though she were suspended in a place where no distressing thoughts could reach her.

Chet was good company, cheerful, funny and bursting with enthusiasm. He never mentioned Josh's name or brought up the real reason Kristin was in Washington. She was a tourist, and he was her very knowledgeable guide. They had a marvelous time.

The bubble burst after dinner on the third night.

Standing in Kristin's hotel room after a busy day of

sight-seeing, Chet cleared his throat and shoved his hands into his pockets.

"Kristin," he said, "Quinn's fever's gone. He's being released from the hospital with orders to have rest and quiet."

Kristin stood statue-still across the room, staring at Chet. "I see."

"The three of us will be flying to Maine tomorrow afternoon. I'll pick you up at one."

"Yes, all right," she said, knowing the color had drained from her face. "Well," she added, a trifle too loudly, "I can't thank you enough for spending so much time with me showing me the city and—"

"Kristin, everything is going to be fine."

"Is it?" She could hear the trembling in her voice. "Oh, I realize that Josh and I will be cleared of any wrongdoing, but beyond that? No, it isn't going to be fine."

"You, um," Chet started, appearing slightly embarrassed. "You're in love with Quinn, aren't you?"

"It's not important whether I am or not." She walked to the sofa and sat down. "It just doesn't matter, Chet."

"Love is always important," he said, smiling. "My mama told me that." He headed for the door. "I'll see you tomorrow, Kristin. You just think about it."

"Goodbye," Kristin said softly as the door closed behind him. Love *was* always important, Kristin thought, but without trust there could be no love.

Kristin sighed and leaned her head back on the top of the sofa, staring up at the ceiling. Images of Josh danced in her mind. Images so real it was as though she could reach out and touch him.

She raised her head, chasing the vivid pictures away. Josh didn't love her; he didn't even trust her! And in actuality she really didn't trust *him* anymore. No, without trust they had nothing. What they'd had, and what might have been, was over.

With dragging steps and an ache in her heart, Kristin went into the bathroom and a short time later was relaxing in a hot bubble bath.

Tomorrow, she thought over and over. She and Josh were flying to Maine, going to her house, tomorrow. Well, so be it. She'd pretend she was Scarlett O'Hara and worry about it then.

The flight to Maine was uneventful. The drive to Kristin's was uneventful. And quiet, since Josh slept during both trips. Except for a mumbled greeting when he'd arrived at the airport, having been driven by one of his huge guards from the hospital, Josh hadn't spoken.

Chet had woken him when they'd landed, and Josh had gotten into the car as though in a fog, then promptly fallen asleep again. Chet had little to say, which was unusual for him, and Kristin was left on her own to grow tenser with every passing mile.

When Chet pulled into Kristin's driveway, she felt as if it had been months since she'd been inside her cozy home. She needed to see it, she realized. Needed to allow its welcoming warmth to wrap around her.

She hurried to the front door as Chet collected the luggage. Josh yawned and slowly got out of the car, staring at the house.

Home, he thought. He was home. He was also, to his own disgust, nervous as hell. He'd slept during the flight, then pretended to be asleep as they'd driven to Kristin's. This plan was nuts! But it was all he had.

"Kristin is uptight," Chet said under his breath as he came up to Josh.

"She's not the only one," Josh said. "This is borderline insane."

"Have you no faith? It's brilliant. I gave up vacation time to pull this off, Quinn. You blow it and I'm going to be really ticked. So far your sparkling conversation has been outstanding."

"Hell, I didn't know what to say to her. I have to think this through, do it right. I've been lying in that hospital bed making up speeches, all of which sounded like garbage. I swear, this is the toughest assignment I've ever had."

"With the best reward. Let's go in. My call should be coming through soon, and then you'll be on your own."

"Why does that sound like bad news?"

Chet laughed. "I can't believe you, Quinn. You're one of the sharpest, toughest agents in the world and you're shaking in your shorts."

"Yeah, well, I'd rather go up against six Koltsovs than one Kristin Duquesne with tears in her eyes."

"You've got a point there. Come on. It's cold out here."

Inside the house, Kristin was putting the screen in front of a roaring fire on the hearth. She turned to face the two men as they entered.

"There," she said, smiling brightly. "Isn't a fire nice on a nippy day like this?" Do not look at Josh, she told herself. Do not remember what you've shared in that room. "Just put the suitcases down, Chet. We'll figure out sleeping arrangements later."

She was talking too fast, Josh realized, and had yet to look at him. This definitely wasn't going well.

Kristin rushed on. "Now, I thought I'd make a pot of coffee or—"

"Or hot chocolate?" Josh interjected, his voice low.

Kristin's gaze flew to Josh's face as she remembered what had transpired when she'd fixed them hot chocolate with whipped cream on top. And remembered . . .

A flutter of desire began deep within her and swept over her, showing itself in a warm flush on her cheeks. She told herself to look away from Josh's dark, mesmerizing eyes, but she couldn't move. She told herself to march into the kitchen and make coffee—not hot chocolate—but she couldn't move. And she told herself not to stand there, aching to feel Josh's strong arms wrap her in the safe haven of his embrace, but she simply couldn't move.

The telephone rang.

Kristin gasped, her hand flying to her heart. She hurried to the desk and lifted the receiver. "Hello?"

"Chet Bell, please," a man said.

"Yes, hold on." She turned to look at Chet. "It's for you."

Chet crossed the room to take the receiver from her, and Kristin headed for the kitchen without looking at Josh.

"Going into the kitchen?" he said.

"Yes, to make coffee," she said, not halting her step. "That's all that's on the menu, Mr. Quinn." She disappeared into the kitchen.

"*Ten* Koltsovs," Josh muttered, "would be easier than this."

Chet replaced the receiver and smiled, giving Josh the thumbs-up sign.

"Oh, Kristin?" Chet called. "Could you come in here for a moment?"

Kristin appeared at the kitchen door, then walked several feet into the living room and stopped. "Yes?"

"I've just been given new orders," Chet said. "An emergency has developed, and they're rounding up everyone who isn't on a vitally important case. My being here is just a formality. Official procedure, you understand. Everyone knows you two will be cleared by the board of inquiry."

"You're leaving?" Kristin said, knowing her voice was squeaking.

"Yep," Chet said, nodding. He looked at Josh. "Guess I'll have to haul you back to the hospital, Quinn."

"Not a chance," Josh said.

"Hey, your orders are as official as mine," Chet said. "You're to have rest and quiet. Until you're checked over and released by a doctor of the Feds, you have to follow those orders."

"I'm not going to the hospital," Josh said. "I don't care what my orders are. I can rest somewhere else."

"Kristin's is the only place they've agreed to," Chet said.

Both Josh and Chet looked at Kristin.

Oh, no, she thought, her mind racing. They were waiting for her to open her mouth and say that Josh could stay there even though Chet was leaving. Well, ha! No way. She didn't want Josh Quinn there. Yes, she did. No, she did not!

"I guess you'd better stay here, Josh," she said.

"Great," Chet said. "Well, I'm off. I hope I'll see you again sometime, Kristin."

"Yes, that would be nice," she said lamely. "Take care of yourself, Chet."

"Sure thing. See ya, Quinn."

"Yeah, see ya," Josh said.

Chet picked up his suitcase and beat a hasty retreat out the door. Once he'd driven away, the only sound in the living room was the crackling of the fire.

Kristin looked at Josh. Josh looked at Kristin. Waves of awareness, of sensuality, as heated as the flames in the fireplace seemed to weave back and forth between them. Heartbeats quickened. Desire pulsed deep and low, demanding attention.

"Kristin," Josh said, his voice slightly gritty, "we have to talk."

"No," she said, shaking her head, "there's nothing to say, nothing I want to hear. The trust is gone, Josh, and with it went everything else."

Josh drew a deep breath and let it out slowly before he spoke again. "Kristin, I love you."

"Without trust there just isn't anything to build on— What?" she said, her eyes widening.

He crossed the room and cradled her face in his hands, gazing down into her eyes.

"I love you," he said again. "I love you. I need you. And I want to make love to you."

"You...you love me? No, you don't. You can't. How could you if you don't even trust me? I trusted you, and you crushed that trust. Damn you, Joshua Quinn, why are you doing this?"

"Because it's true," he said, stroking his thumbs back and forth over her cheeks. "I'm not saying it to try to lure you into bed with me. I'm saying it because it's the truth. I never doubted you, Kristin. I told Fred Jones a thousand times that you were innocent, shouldn't be brought in for questioning the way you were. I was mad as hell that they put you through that."

"But—"

"I know you think the trust between us has been destroyed, but it hasn't. It's there, and I'm going to prove it to you. I've never loved before, Kristin." He lowered his head toward hers. "I love you." He brushed his lips over hers. "I love you so damn much."

And she loved him! Kristin thought. Oh, heaven help her, she did. But she had so many questions, so many doubts, and—

Josh claimed her mouth with his, and all rational thought fled from Kristin's mind.

Oh, yes, her heart whispered. Oh, yes, Josh, yes.

He was seducing her, he knew it, and it probably wasn't fair, but Josh didn't care. He loved her, needed her by his side for all time, ached with the want of her. He would show her, prove to her that trusting him wasn't wrong. It was very, very right. He was fighting the toughest battle ever—the battle of his life—and he intended to win. He couldn't, wouldn't, lose Kristin Duquesne.

The kiss that had begun as soft and sensuous became hungry and urgent. It was give-and-take; it was Kristin and Josh—wanting.

Josh's hands roamed over the fleecy material of Kristin's sweater, down to the slope of her bottom. He nestled her against him, the cradle of his hips welcoming her and announcing his arousal. His tongue delved into her mouth, meeting hers, tasting, savoring the familiar and longed-for sweetness. A groan of need caught in his throat.

Kristin circled Josh's neck with her arms, inching her fingers into his thick hair. She answered the demands of his lips and tongue but wanted more, wanted all of him. The confusion in her mind was pushed aside. The future was a blur. The moment was now.

Josh's breathing was rough as he moved to trail a ribbon of kisses along Kristin's throat and slipped his hands under the waistband of her sweater, then upward to splay them on her back. Her breasts were crushed to his chest, her soft curves molded to his heated, aching body. *Never* had he desired a woman as he did Kristin. But never before had he loved.

"Kristin," he murmured, "I want you. I want to make love to you. Now."

"Yes," she whispered. "Oh, yes, Josh, I want you, too."

He gave her one more kiss, a mind-drugging kiss, then led her down the hall to the bedroom. He turned on the small lamp on the nightstand to cast a rosy glow over the darkening room, flipped back the blankets on the bed, then turned to her.

Their eyes met and held, messages of desire sent and received.

"Josh, I..." Kristin started, her voice unsteady, "I...think I should tell you that I'm not very experienced. I mean, I haven't known very many...that is..."

Josh gave her a tender, gentle, loving smile, then drew her into the safe circle of his arms.

"I know that," he said, weaving his fingers through her silken hair. "That makes you very special, and I feel very honored. I love you, Kristin. I've never been with a woman I've loved, so this is a new experience for me, too. We're going to be fantastic together."

She loved him so much, Kristin thought. Be it right or be it wrong, she loved him. Nothing else mattered.

Josh moved back only far enough that he could draw her sweater up and away, then dropped it and her bra on the floor. He settled his gaze on the lush fullness of her breasts, and with visibly shaking hands he filled his palms with her feminine bounty.

"So beautiful," he said, lowering his head to draw one nipple deep into his mouth.

A soft sigh of pleasure whispered from Kristin's lips as wondrous sensations swirled within her. She gripped Josh's shoulders for support as her knees be-

gan to tremble. Josh gave the same tantalizing attention to her other breast, and she closed her eyes to
savor his foray. When he lifted his head, she instantly
missed the sweet torture of his mouth.

Josh pulled his own sweater off, and the stark white
of the bandage on his side contrasted sharply with his
burnished skin. As Kristin watched his every movement, he quickly shed his remaining clothes to stand
naked before her.

Kristin's heart nearly burst with love as she realized
that Josh had purposely offered himself to her first,
made himself bare and vulnerable first. With a soft
smile she slid her slacks and panties down her legs and
stepped out of them, pushing off her shoes in the pro-
cess. As she straightened, she took in every inch of
Josh's magnificent body, then met his gaze steadily.

"You're beautiful, too, Josh," she said.

He smiled. "I'm a walking bruise."

"Beautiful bruises."

He pulled her to him, burying his face in her hair.
"I want this to be so good for you, perfect for you.
I've been waiting a lifetime for you, Kristin, and I
didn't even know it. In my world we all know that
nothing, no one, must ever touch our soul, but you
have, and…and it's warm, so unbelievably warm…."

They moved onto the bed, Josh stretching out next
to her, resting on his arm so that he could see all of her
clearly, his heated gaze traveling over her dewy skin.
He claimed her mouth in a fiery kiss as he moved his
hand to her flat stomach, then lower, then lower yet.

Kristin was awash with desire like none she had ever
known. Arching toward him, seeking more, she

moaned at the pure ecstasy of being touched and kissed by Josh.

"Oh, Josh," she gasped as he captured the bud of one breast in his mouth. He suckled in a rhythmic pull that was matched by a pulsing, liquid heat deep within her. "Josh, please..."

Josh held back, his muscles quivering with the forced restraint as he continued to tantalize and tease, kiss and caress Kristin until she was writhing on the bed, her voice a near sob.

"Josh!"

"Yes!"

He moved over her, resting on his arms as he gazed down at her flushed face. She looked at him, her eyes smoky with desire.

And then he came to her, entering her slowly, waiting for her body to adjust to him before he thrust deeper into her honeyed warmth, which received him fully, completely, perfectly.

"Kristin," he groaned, then began to move in a steady tempo.

She matched his rhythm, glorying in all that he was, all that she was, all that they were together. As one. Their bodies strained against each other, their senses merged as they neared the summit of their climb.

"Josh!"

"Oh, yes!"

A wild heartbeat apart, they reached the top, each seeming to be hurled into a place that was beyond description in its beauty. They called each other's names as they hovered somewhere above the here and now. And then they slowly returned.

"Oh, Josh," Kristin said, framing his face in her hands, "that was—was so wonderful."

"I knew it would be—with you." He brushed his lips over hers, then moved off her, pulling the blankets up to cover them both. He tucked her close to his side, nestling her head on his shoulder.

"You didn't hurt your side, did you?" Kristin asked.

"No, it's fine. Are you all right?"

"More than all right. Oh, Josh, I've never experienced anything so completely beautiful as our lovemaking. There just aren't words to describe it."

"Yeah, I know...what you...mean." His eyes drifted closed.

She laughed softly. "You're so tired. Sleep. We'll have dinner later."

He opened his eyes. "I don't think it's very romantic to fall asleep on you two seconds after... Man, I'm beat. This is ridiculous. Kristin, we have to talk and—"

"We will, but they told you in the hospital that you needed a lot of rest. So...sleep."

"Mmm," he said, his eyes closing again. "Maybe just for a minute."

Sleep claimed him in the next breath, and for the following half hour Kristin watched him, simply lay close to his heat and strength and gazed at him.

How she loved this man, she thought dreamily. What had been missing from her life had been found in the form of Joshua Quinn. The void within her was filled by the essence of him and his love for her. It wasn't perfect, but she'd long ago acknowledged that life never was.

Perfect would be, she decided, to have Josh with her every day, every night. Perfect would be to have him there as she grew big with his child. Perfect would be to have no nagging doubts in the deep recesses of her mind.

But the doubts were there.

Josh seemed to realize, she mused, that her trust in him—and therefore in them as one—had been shattered. He had spoken of proving her wrong, of showing her that what they had together was real and honest.

But it was frightening, Kristin admitted. She now knew that there were times when she didn't know where Josh Quinn, who had moved through life alone, left off and Josh, the man who said he needed her by his side, began. The two became intertwined, causing the doubts, the fears, as she questioned what was real and what was a role he was acting out.

She hated the confusion, the doubts. She just wanted to love this man and savor the knowledge that he loved her in return. That would be perfect. But life never was.

With a sigh, Kristin carefully slipped out of bed and pulled on a robe. She pushed her feet into slippers and gazed at Josh for a long moment, then left the room. After adding several logs to the fire, she went into the kitchen to start dinner. She defrosted some meat in the microwave oven, took vegetables from the refrigerator and began to prepare a stew.

An hour later, delicious aromas wafted through the air. Josh appeared in the kitchen doorway, dressed in his jeans and sweater.

"Something smells good," he said.

"Stew and corn bread," Kristin said, smiling at him. "You had a good nap."

"Ridiculous nap. All I do these days is sleep." He paused, then crossed the room to stand beside her. "Well, among other things."

"Very nice other things," she said, laughing softly. "Ready to eat?"

"I'll help you," he said, kissing the pulse beating at her temple.

"No, just sit."

"I'm not an invalid, Kristin," he said gruffly.

She looked up at him in surprise. "I realize that, Josh, but dinner is all ready. There's nothing for you to do."

He raked a hand through his hair. "I'm sorry. I just hated being trapped in that hospital bed. I don't like the idea that I still haven't got much energy."

"You'll bounce back quickly, Josh. The doctor said you were in excellent condition before all this happened, and that's in your favor. You're just going to have to be a little patient. You'll be in top form in no time—you'll see."

"And ready to get on with my life," he said as they sat down at the table.

"Yes. Help yourself to the stew."

Josh filled his plate, then buttered a square of corn bread. They ate in silence for several minutes.

"You must be looking forward to getting busy in your studio," he said finally. "You were rather rudely interrupted, to say the least."

"Yes, there's a lot I want to accomplish before my vacation is over and the Christmas rush begins. The inventory of my own work is very low at the gallery."

"Painting is a very private thing, isn't it? I mean, you prefer to be alone while you do it."

She shrugged. "I don't know. I've never thought about it. I live alone, so I paint alone. I don't see why it would disturb me if someone was in the house or even in the same room. In fact, now that I think about it, Carol sat and chattered at me once while I was painting. It didn't bother me."

"I just wondered. I wouldn't want to be in your way."

"You'd never be in my way, Josh."

He shrugged.

"You're not used to sitting still for very long, are you?" she said.

"No. I've been banged up a few times and had to lie low. It drives me nuts. I'll quit taking it out on you, though."

"Yes, well, I can understand your frustration," Kristin said, poking at her stew with her fork. "After all, you have a very exciting life out there."

"I wouldn't call it exciting, actually," he said.

Kristin looked up at him. "How did you become an agent, Josh?"

"It was a long time ago, Kristin."

"Do you mind telling me?"

He studied her face for a long moment, as though struggling to come to a decision. "I guess I don't mind. I was abandoned by my father when I was twelve. My mother had left years before. It was in Chicago. I came home from school and my father was gone. No note, no...anything. He left a ten-dollar bill on the table in our tenement."

"That's terrible," Kristin whispered.

"I stayed there until the landlord kicked me out, then I lived on the streets. I managed to go to school for a few years by faking addresses. I did odd jobs, stole food, lived in warehouses, empty buildings, wherever."

"The cold," Kristin said, her eyes widening. "That's why you hate the cold."

"Yeah," he said, his voice raspy. "During the winter I was . . . was always so damn cold."

"Oh, Josh," she said, covering his hand with hers on the top of the table.

He immediately slipped his hand free, his jaw tightening slightly. "I did all right. I was big for my age, and at sixteen I lied through my teeth and joined the army. I did three tours in Vietnam, then was approached by the agency. I was taken under the wing of a man named Hudson. He fine-tuned the training I'd gotten in the army. He was the only one before you who ever called me Joshua."

"This Hudson—where is he now?"

"He's dead," Josh said, his voice low and flat. "We got caught in a double cross, and he was shot. He was like a father to me by then. I didn't want to leave him, but they were closing in on us. He said I had to go."

Tears filled Kristin's eyes.

"Hudson gave me the gold lighter. He told me I was a killer, that I could never change who and what I was and I was always to remember that. He taught me the code of survival. He taught me that no one should ever touch me."

The tears spilled onto Kristin's cheeks. "You said...you said that I've touched your soul, Josh. Are you sorry I have?"

"No! Oh, no, Kristin, don't ever think that. I was so cold—inside—and you've given me a warmth like nothing I've ever known."

"Josh, do you believe what Hudson said? I mean, don't you think that people can change?"

"I don't know about people in general, Kristin, but *I* intend to change. Don't you remember me telling you that I wanted to teach?"

"Yes," she said, frowning. "I remember, but when you told me that I believed you were a computer troubleshooter. I assume that all of what you told me then was part of the role you were playing."

"No, I do want to teach. There are young agents coming in all the time who could benefit from what I've learned. I'm tired of working in the field, Kristin. I've had enough, want to settle down in one place, which in this case would be Washington, where the training is done." He paused. "Wait a minute. Let's back up here. Kristin, what we shared before you knew who I really was wasn't part of my assignment. I kissed you, held you, because I wanted to, not because I was told to. I thought you knew that."

She leaned toward him. "Oh, Josh, don't you see? It's all gotten muddled up together, and I don't know how to separate it anymore. When I thought you didn't trust me, then realized I'd been wrong in trusting and believing in you, I was shattered. I can't seem to put the pieces back together."

"I understand," he said. He covered her hand with his on top of the table. "Kristin, do you love me?"

"Yes," she whispered, "but unless the trust is there it won't matter how I feel."

He studied their joined hands for a long moment, then looked at her again. "Will you give us some time, give us—give me—a chance to prove that what we have is real?"

"I . . . Yes, Josh, I will."

"Good. We'll take one day at a time for now," he said, stroking her wrist with his thumb. "We'll enjoy each day, make love each night, just be who we are. Okay?"

"Okay," she said, managing a small smile.

"Oh, God, you look so frightened," he said, shaking his head. "I know what it took for you to trust me after what happened when you were engaged. I cherished that trust, Kristin, and I'm going to prove to you all over again that I deserve it. Remember that the bottom line is that I love you."

"I'll remember, Josh," she said softly.

He looked at her for another long moment, then nodded before redirecting his attention to his dinner. They completed the meal in silence.

"I'm afraid I don't have anything for dessert," Kristin said finally. "I need to go to the grocery store tomorrow and stock up."

"I'll go with you. I can't remember when I've been in a grocery store. I'll enjoy it. Oh, and I imagine you'd like to see if Magic Lady is around. I swear, that is one arrogant cat."

"Oh, yes, I'd love to see her. The last time I held her she was . . . I don't know . . . lumpy. I wonder if she's going to have kittens. Wouldn't that be fun?"

"Fun?" Josh said, his eyebrows shooting up. "No, I don't see it qualifying under the heading of 'fun.'"

"Oh, Josh, kittens are so cute, fuzzy, playful. Goodness, I'd better stop talking about this or I'll be terribly disappointed if she doesn't have babies."

"Well, suppose she did," he said, crossing his arms over his chest. "What I want to know is, how many of those kittens do you plan to keep for yourself? I'd have to get a second job with all those mouths to feed. A man's work is never done!"

Kristin laughed delightedly, relieved that the earlier tension had passed. "Just one kitten, I promise. Oh, and, of course, Magic Lady stays. That's not so bad, is it? Oh, I hope she's pregnant. I adore babies."

Josh picked up his coffee mug, wrapped both his hands around it and peered at her over the rim.

"Just kitten-type babies?" he said casually. "Or are you into other kinds, too?"

"Puppies are nice," Kristin said, her smile widening.

"Anything else?" he said, leaning slightly toward her.

"Mr. Quinn, are you trying to find out how I feel about human babies?"

"Yeah," he said, grinning at her. "How am I doing?"

"Lousy. For a seasoned agent, you're not very adept at wiggling information out of someone."

"Well, I've never asked an enemy agent how he felt about having my baby," he said, a trifle too loudly. "The subject just never came up, Miss Duquesne."

Kristin laughed. "Oh, I see." She became serious and smiled at him warmly. "I love you, Josh. Nothing would make me happier than to have your baby."

He reached for her hand and cradled it in both of his. "You're incredible. I never allowed myself to think about things like love, a special woman, having a child with that lady. It was a world closed to me, locked behind a heavy door, and I didn't have the key, never would. I didn't let it matter. I just went through life alone. But then there you were, Kristin, and everything changed. Something happened to me from the moment you opened that door on the very first night. Something wonderful and . . . very, very warm. I love you, Kristin."

"And I love you, Josh."

"Kristin, listen to me, okay? What I know about love, being in love, could fit into that fancy thimble we're both well acquainted with. A part of me wants to ask you to marry me—now. No, *demand* that you marry me, so that I know you're really mine and I'm yours, we're connected, committed. But . . ." He frowned.

"But . . ." she prompted him.

"But another section of my mind says that's wrong, that I'd be rushing things, that we need a chance to relax, just live our lives together for a while, like I said we would. You say you'd like to have my baby, but I know it isn't going to happen unless you learn to trust me again." He shook his head. "Damn." He pulled his cigarettes from his pocket and lighted one with the gold lighter.

Kristin sighed. "I guess I shouldn't have said what I did about our having a baby. It's just that sometimes I get so swept up in how I feel about you, us, what we could have together if... But then it all comes out of the shadows, taunting me with the doubts, and I get so frightened."

"I know," Josh said. "That's why this time that we're spending together is important to us. It has to be real and honest and open. Understand?"

"Yes," she said, nodding.

"So if there's anything you'd like to say, you just open your mouth and say it."

"Well," she said, getting to her feet, "at the moment I'd better say I'm about to clean the kitchen."

Josh chuckled, but his smile faded as he watched Kristin cross the room, his mind sorting through what she had said. He should grab her and run, he thought. Take her to a justice of the peace and make her his wife as quickly as possible.

Wrong. They needed time together—normal people-in-love-living-their-lives time. Time to rebuild Kristin's trust in him. Their entire future was at stake here. He'd have to be patient. But, thank God, she loved him. That in itself was a precious gift.

"You know, Kristin," he said, "people will talk because I'm staying here."

"I don't care."

"Are you sure?"

"Trust me, Josh."

"Trust you?" he repeated. How could she say that when she didn't trust *him*? Don't push her, Quinn, he told himself. "Never mind. Would you like me to load the dishwasher?"

"No, thank you, I'm just about finished here."

"All right," he said, getting to his feet. "We'll meet in front of the fire."

"Okay," she said smiling, reaching for the large pan on the stove as Josh left the kitchen. It was one day at a time for now, she mused. So be it.

The remainder of the evening was relaxed and comfortable, as though when they left the kitchen they also left behind the reasons for the serious conversation they'd had regarding their relationship. They sat close together on the sofa in front of the fire, chatting, falling silent, talking again.

Josh told Kristin about the exotic foods he'd eaten in foreign countries, and she wrinkled her nose in disgust at some of the things he described. He asked her more about her love of painting, as well as about other forms of art, and she agreed to give him a tour of the gallery.

It was a lovely time, a sharing time, and to Kristin it spoke of the kind of life she wanted to have with this man. She wanted him there with her at the end of each day, talking, laughing, being close. She wanted to shop for groceries with Josh, play with kittens, discuss names for the child they would create.

Oh, yes, she thought wistfully, this was what she wanted with Josh.

Josh slipped his hand to the nape of Kristin's neck, bringing her out of her reverie. "Tired?" he asked. "You've become very quiet."

"No, just thinking. You're the one who should be tired."

"Nope. I had a ridiculous nap, remember? I'm—" he lowered his head toward hers, his gaze on her slightly parted lips "—definitely not tired."

"Oh...good," she said, hearing the breathlessness in her own voice.

Josh inched closer, his warm breath feathering over Kristin's lips, but he didn't claim her mouth. She shivered with sensual anticipation of what would come. He nipped at her lower lip, then lightly kissed one corner of her mouth, then the other. Then, with the tip of his tongue, he outlined her lips in a slow, tantalizing journey.

"Josh," Kristin said, managing only a whisper, "if you don't kiss me, really kiss me, in the next two seconds, I'm going to dissolve."

He chuckled softly, slid his arm around her waist and took full possession of her mouth, his tongue delving deep within.

Oh, yes, Kristin thought dreamily. Josh...

Then all thoughts fled as passions soared and clothes seemed to float away. Josh pulled Kristin gently down to lie on the plush rug in front of the fire. His gaze skimmed over her, the heat of his desire surpassing that of the flames in the fireplace. He stretched out next to her, resting on one arm and splaying a hand on her flat stomach.

His child, he thought, would grow in there, created by both Kristin and him, a tiny miracle resulting from their love for each other. Incredible.

Kristin watched as Josh's eyes glowed with tenderness and warmth. She saw the burnished tone of his hand against her pale skin, felt the heat of it swirling within her and knew his mind had traveled the same path as hers. A baby. Theirs. The very thought of it was beautiful, nearly overwhelming.

"Josh," she whispered.

He turned his head to meet her gaze, and it was as though they could read the messages in each other's hearts. They knew without speaking that their thoughts had centered on the child they wished to be born of their love. It was a moment of sharing that held depths beyond any they had known, a moment separate and apart from the desire surging through them.

"Kristin," he said, his voice husky.

He kissed her gently, reverently, as though she were made of china more delicate than that of the thimble. He moved his hand over her soft body as though discovering its mysteries for the first time.

This was his woman, Josh thought. She herself was a miracle, a gift, that had touched his soul and changed his life forever. This was Kristin, and he loved her.

As Josh kissed and caressed her, Kristin because increasingly aware of her own femininity. She let her hands roam over the corded muscles of Josh's back, shoulders and arms, marveling at his strength, the perfection of his rugged body. Such contrasts she and Josh were, counterparts, complete within themselves and each enhanced by the addition of the other.

Oh, he was beautiful, this man, Kristin mused dreamily. When the time was right she would carry his child nestled safely within her. He had touched her as she had him, and she loved him.

Josh lifted his lips from hers, then moved to one breast, gently drawing the nipple deep into his mouth. With a sense of awe and wonder, Josh let his hand travel lower, seeking and finding the moist heat of Kristin's femininity, which spoke of her desire for him, the readiness of her body to receive him. Oh, yes, Kristin Duquesne was a miracle.

"Josh, come to me," she said softly. "Please."

He gazed into her eyes as he joined their bodies.

"Kristin, I—"

"I know," she said, her voice hushed. "Oh, yes, Josh, I know. Tonight is so special, so very beautiful."

He thrust deep within her and began the tempo. She instantly matched it. Slowly, steadily, they felt the pressure build and, with it, the anticipation of the glorious sensations they would experience as they reached their climaxes. Together. Again without speaking, they knew that on this night it was so very important that they give and receive the ultimate gift of their union at the same time. And they did.

"Josh!"

"Yes, now, Kristin."

Tremors swept through them as they held each other tightly, each feeling what the other felt, each relishing their shared release.

"Oh, Joshua."

They hovered in a place with no name, then languorously floated back to reality, still one entity.

Neither spoke.

Words could not describe what they had shared, so they were quiet, savoring, remembering, rejoicing.

Later, in unspoken agreement, they gathered their clothes and went into the bedroom. They reached for each other in the same instant to rekindle the flame of passion, which was still a glowing ember.

It was far into the night before they slept.

Nine

The following few days were, Kristin decided, the stuff of which honeymoons were made. It was as though a rosy glow had settled over her and Josh's little piece of the world, shielding them from everything beyond their space. Within that delightful sphere were only smiles, laughter, precious hours spent together and lovemaking beyond description in its beauty.

Josh, to Kristin's continued amazement and delight, seemed to find great pleasure in the ordinary and mundane activities that went along with filling the hours of a day.

The trip to the small grocery store in Temple had been a major event. Josh had refused to be hurried, wanting to examine all the crammed shelves had to offer. The cart was soon piled high with snacks and junk food, and Kristin had to get her own cart to hold the meat, fresh fruit and vegetables. When Josh had insisted on purchasing both smooth and chunky peanut butter, Kristin had rolled her eyes heavenward and said she'd never seen him before in her life.

Josh's energy was still far below the level he was accustomed to, and he was none too pleased when fatigue forced him to rest, which usually resulted in his falling asleep. In an act of stubborn defiance he refused to nap on the bed, stating that it made him feel like a kid being sent to his room. Instead he sprawled on the sofa as Kristin hid her smile, shook her head and retreated to her studio bedroom to paint.

Four days after their return from Washington, a startled Josh found Magic Lady serenely providing lunch for two kittens on the throw rug in the laundry room.

"Kristin!" he yelled. "You'd better come in here."

Kristin hurried into the room, then smiled delightedly. "Oh, she did it! They're so cute."

"They look like scrawny mice," Josh said, leaning over for a more thorough inspection. "Weird."

"Joshua, really. You never insult a mother's babies. They'll be adorable as soon as they fill out a bit. Magic Lady looks so proud of herself."

"Well, I'll give her that," he said, nodding. "Having babies, even if they do look like mice instead of kittens, is no small accomplishment. Even in this age of equality, it's something a man can never do. He's there at the beginning and can witness the birth, but during the months in between all he can do is stand by and watch, try his best to be supportive. I think that at times a guy must feel pretty helpless while his wife is pregnant.''

Kristin circled his waist with her arms, careful to avoid the wound in his side, and smiled up at him. ''She knows he's there, Josh, and that must mean a great deal. They created that child together.''

''Right. The man's part is pure pleasure. He says he understands when she doesn't feel well or is tired or gets as big as a whale.''

''And she believes that he *does* understand.''

''Why?''

''Because she loves him and trusts him and...'' She frowned.

Josh wove his fingers through her hair. ''Exactly. That's the point I was trying to get you to realize. You've said you want to have my baby, Kristin. Do you see how much trust is involved in that?''

''Yes. Yes, I do.''

''Then we're coming along just fine here.''

''Yes,'' she said, smiling, ''I think maybe we are. Josh, I've never been kissed in a laundry room.''

''You poor, deprived person,'' he said, then captured her mouth with his.

The kiss was long and powerful, and Kristin's cheeks were flushed when Josh finally lifted his head.

''Oh, my,'' she said breathlessly.

''That's all you get for now,'' he said, smiling at her. ''You said you wanted to paint this afternoon. So goodbye. Go paint.''

''What are you going to do?''

''Get out of this laundry room, for starters, before I try to figure out a way to make love to you on top of the washing machine. Come on." He took her hand and led her into the kitchen, then turned to face her. "Kristin, there's something I'd like to say."

"Yes?"

"On the day we came back here, I told you that I tried to keep you from being brought in for questioning, that I knew you were innocent of any wrongdoing. You've never commented on my saying that. I need to know if you believe me."

"Josh, I ... Can't we just put all that behind us?"

"No, Kristin, we can't," he said, shoving his hands into the back pockets of his jeans. "That would be like putting a Band-Aid on an open wound, which would mean you might ignore it for a while, but it would still be there. I know you have doubts about my actions while I was carrying out that assignment. We have to talk about those doubts and put them to rest once and for all."

"I thought we were starting fresh, Josh. Everything has been so wonderful these past few days. Why drag up those painful memories?"

He lifted his hands to grip her upper arms. "Because they shouldn't be painful. I've gone over everything a hundred times in my mind, and I can't think of anything I've kept from you. Even more important is that every word I've said has been the truth. There are ghosts standing in the way of our future together, Kristin. Ghosts that have no business being there, because your doubts about me, what I did, are unfounded. I know you've been betrayed in the past, but not by me, never by me."

Kristin stepped back, forcing him to drop his hands from her arms. "Why are you doing this?" she said, wrapping her hands around her elbows. "You said we were going to have time, but now you're pushing me to accept the deception simply because you said it was all necessary to carry out your assignment."

"It *was* necessary. But you also know I overstepped my authority and told you the truth because I valued your trust and couldn't bear to see you scared out of your mind. I've explained every detail I can think of, trying to put all the ghosts to rest."

"You rationalized your actions, Josh. There's a tremendous difference there. What about the future? Do you think you can rationalize away any mode of conduct, pat me on the head and expect me to accept whatever you do or say, no questions asked?"

"Damn it, no, of course not," he said, raking a hand through his hair. "You're twisting things around."

"I'm trying to learn from my past mistakes," she said, her voice rising. "When I found the man I was engaged to in bed with another woman, I turned and walked away. He came charging after me as he pulled on his pants, yelling at me that I was overreacting. He rationalized it, you see, saying that all men have a little fun on the side, that it doesn't mean anything, and why wouldn't I believe that? He was, after all, he hollered, telling me the truth."

"I'm...not...that...man," Josh said slowly through clenched teeth.

"I know that! You're not fighting his ghost, but you are expecting me to accept everything you say on blind faith. I'm trying, Josh. I really am," she said, tears welling up in her eyes. "But I remember how you came in here telling me you were a computer expert, a longtime friend of Jeff Jameson's, how you convinced me you had no utilities so you could spend the night and plant those listening devices."

"I had no choice!" he roared.

"And in the middle of all of that you kissed me, Joshua. You kissed me and held me, and I felt so special, and—"

"Damn it, Kristin, I've explained it all to you over and over. I swore to you that what had happened between us was real, and you said you believed me. You said you trusted me."

"I did! But then Chet took me to Washington like I was a criminal, and it was too much. It all just came crashing down on me. It's a jumbled maze of questions and doubts and not knowing what is real anymore." Two tears slid down her cheeks.

Josh planted his hands on his narrow hips and stared up at the ceiling for a long moment before looking at her again.

"Kristin," he said, his voice low, "you're telling me you're afraid I'll conduct myself however I choose, then try to explain it away like it's no big deal." He frowned and shook his head. "But have you listened, really listened, to what you're saying to *me*? You're using your trust like a weapon against me."

"What?" she said, wiping the tears from her cheeks.

"You told me you believed me when I said that what we'd shared in this house was real. But now?" He gave a sharp, bitter-sounding laugh. "Now you've decided that you're not so sure, that the jury is still out. Is this how our life would be? I'm late coming home and I explain I was held up in traffic. Fine. But the next day you withdraw the trust and announce you no longer believe I was held up in traffic, so where the hell was I?"

"Josh, I—"

"I can't live that way!" he said, bringing his fist down heavily on the countertop. Kristin jumped. "I can't come through the door every night wondering if you're going to hug me or hit me over the head with your lack-of-trust board. Ah, damn, don't you see? We're supposed to be talking about love here. Love, Kristin. Commitment, faith and trust in each other." A shudder ripped through him. "I wonder," he said, his voice husky, "if you understand what love is."

"I—"

"I'm talking about forever," he went on, taking a step backward, "but I can't spend forever on trial. I think...I think you'd better figure out whether you really do love me, then take it further and ask yourself if you know what love means." He spun around and started for the kitchen door. "I'm going for a walk."

"But—" She flinched as she heard the front door slam. "You're supposed to be resting and— Oh, Josh, I love you. I do!"

Kristin reached for a kitchen chair and sat down, her trembling legs refusing to hold her a moment longer. A chill swept through her as Josh's words echoed in her mind, beating against her and causing a heavy ache in her heart.

There'd been such pain in Josh's voice and in his eyes. Pain, she knew, that she had caused. The confusion, the doubts that she'd seen as exclusively hers— *her* problems, *her* dilemmas to work through—had lashed out and hurt Josh.

And that, she suddenly realized, was what love was all about.

She was still a separate entity unto herself, she reasoned, yet her life was intertwined with Josh's. What she did and felt and thought affected him, as well as her. They were one not just when they made love but in all facets of their lives. The pain she felt within her over her confusion and doubts was now Josh's pain, as well. When he smiled at her and love shone in his eyes, she was filled with joy, reaping the rewards of what he felt.

Through the darkness and the sunshine, they were one.

Yes, Kristin thought, she understood what love was, what it meant to touch another's soul and have that gentle, glorious touch returned in kind.

And she also knew that unless she gathered her strength, beat the ghosts of doubt, believed in herself and her ability to trust, she was going to lose the love of Joshua Quinn.

Magic Lady wandered out of the laundry room, then purred as she leaned against Kristin's leg. Kristin bent over and stroked the cat.

"I love him, Magic Lady," Kristin whispered. "I really do."

Kristin fed the cat, then went into the living room to peer through the curtains for a sign of Josh. Nothing. Her gaze was drawn to the woods, bringing into crystalline clarity the events surrounding the assignment Josh had had to obtain the package.

She carefully examined each piece of the jumbled puzzle in her mind. Josh jeopardizing his career by telling her what was happening to quiet her fears. Roaring in anger at her having been brought to Washington under suspicion. She could feel the strength of his arms around her as he'd held her tightly, thanking her for her trust in a voice thick with emotion.

And she knew that she loved him with every breath in her body, every beat of her heart.

But . . .

Kristin lifted her chin and waited for the ghosts of doubt to emerge from the shadows and taunt her, jumble the pieces of the puzzle once more.

She waited, but they didn't come.

The ghosts were gone.

She'd won the battle. She was free to live, and free to love Josh.

Her eyes brimming with tears of joy, Kristin looked down the street, willing him to return to the house.

Well, she thought, he'd show up soon enough, when his energy gave out, and she'd tell him that she had at last removed the doubts from her life and his. And in the meantime she'd wait.

Half an hour later Kristin knew that if she didn't find something to do besides stare out the window she was going to become a nervous wreck. She glanced down the street once more, sighed and went into her studio. She propped a blank canvas on the easel, picked up a sketching pencil and cocked her head to one side as she studied the empty expanse.

Ideas, pictures, images, flitted through her mind as she contemplated what she would sketch, then paint in oils.

"Magic Lady," she said, smiling. Magic Lady deserved to have a portrait done of her in acknowledgment of her new role as mother.

A baby, Kristin mused. Oh, yes, she did want to have Josh's baby, and maybe now there was a chance of that dream coming true.

With her cheerful mood restored and hope for a future with Josh renewed, Kristin began to draw on the fine linen.

An hour later, Josh used the expertise he'd learned in his years as an agent to enter the house without a sound. He could now, he decided, add "sneaky" to the long list of less-than-flattering things he'd called himself during his walk.

Why, he'd asked himself over and over, had he pushed Kristin after promising her she would have all the time she needed to sort through her confusion?

As he'd trudged along, ignoring his increasing fatigue, he'd figured out why, and he was none too pleased with the answer.

He was afraid. He was scared to death that he would lose Kristin.

Some irrational part of him had suddenly decided that if he pushed enough he'd win out over her doubts.

That was why he'd forced the issue earlier, he realized. He was a jerk, a total idiot.

Josh glanced in the kitchen and found it empty, then made his way silently down the hall to the studio. He stood in the doorway, his eyes widening as he saw Magic Lady coming to life on the canvas in front of Kristin. He moved into the room.

"I've never seen you paint before," he said quietly.

Kristin spun around. "Josh! You startled me."

His gaze was still riveted on the canvas. "I saw your finished work when you gave me the tour of the gallery, but to see something half finished like this really makes me realize what you're capable of doing."

"Josh, I want to tell you—"

He continued as if she hadn't spoken. "You took something that was empty, blank...." He was still staring at the canvas. "And you're filling it with life and warmth that can never be taken away." He turned his head to meet her gaze. "Kristin, how could I have ever thought you didn't know what love is? You know, because you've done for me what you're doing right there on that canvas. I was empty and so damn cold, and you filled me with love and warmth. I'm sorry. I'm sorry I pushed you. Listen, you'll have all the time I said you'd have and—"

"No," Kristin interrupted. She placed the paints and brush on a small table, then turned back to face him. "No, Josh."

"Kristin, please, I said I was sorry—"

"No, no," she said, shaking her head. "You don't understand. I don't need the time, Josh. Josh, all my doubts are gone. I'm the one who's sorry, and I'm begging you to forgive me for causing you such pain. I love you, Joshua.''

He opened his arms to her. "Come here," he said with a groan.

And she went, with joy and love shining in her eyes and a smile on her lips. She went to be enfolded in the strong, safe haven of Josh's arms and welcomed his mouth as it captured hers.

"You must be tired," she said breathlessly when Josh lifted his head.

"Well, now that you mention it, I could use one of my ridiculous naps. Care to join me?"

"On the sofa?"

"No, I thought I'd stretch out on the bed this time."

"Oh, I see," she said, smiling. "And just how much sleeping are you planning on doing?"

"I'll get around to it—eventually." He circled her shoulders with his arm. "I love you, Kristin."

"And I love you, Josh. I love you and I trust you."

He claimed her mouth in another searing kiss, then led her from the room.

The days passed.

The kittens grew by leaps and bounds, and even Josh admitted that they no longer looked like scrawny mice. Kristin fell in love with a feisty one that was entirely black except for dots of white on its face. She named it Freckles and declared it to be the cutest and most intelligent kitten in the history of kittens. When she came upon Josh snoozing on the sofa with Freckles sound asleep on his chest, Kristin's heart nearly burst with love for him.

The days were serene and peaceful. She and Josh went for walks, shared the cooking and the household chores and never seemed to run out of things to talk about. In the afternoons Kristin worked in her studio while he rested or read in the living room, by the fire. He often wandered in to watch her work, and she had no trouble painting with him looking over her shoulder.

And the nights. How it was possible that their lovemaking could become more and more beautiful, Kristin didn't know. They reached for each other as though it had been days, even weeks, instead of just hours since they'd last become one. Some joinings were urgent, frenzied, nearly rough in the intensity of their need. Others were slow, sweet, sensuous, with hands, lips, teeth and tongues creating exquisite journeys over willing bodies.

Josh took fewer of his famous naps as his strength returned. The multitude of bruises on his body changed color, then finally faded. The wound in his side was sensitive but was healing with no further sign of infection.

On days when there was a clear blue sky they went for drives, exploring the area and discovering small towns tucked away in unexpected places.

One night in front of the fire, a very nervous Josh Quinn officially proposed to Kristin Duquesne. He'd been accepted as a teacher of new agents, he said, and was asking Kristin to move to Washington with him. He knew it meant she would have to sell the gallery in Temple, and if she wanted to think it over—

Before he could complete the sentence, Kristin flung herself into his arms and said she'd be honored to be his wife.

Josh uttered a rather startled "Oh," then appeared thoroughly pleased with himself.

Their lovemaking that night held special meaning, as they realized they had pledged their love—and trust—until death parted them. Their future now held the promise of forever.

Nearly four weeks after they returned from Washington, Kristin awoke, stretched lazily, then automatically reached for Josh. She sat bolt upright on the bed as she realized he wasn't beside her. She pulled on her robe and hurried down the hall to the living room.

Josh was sitting on the sofa, leaning forward with his elbows resting on his knees as he stared into the fire. He had a cup of coffee in his hands.

"Josh?" Kristin said.

He turned to look at her and smiled. "Good morning. I was trying not to wake you. I knew the call would come in early, and I snatched it up as quick as I could."

"The telephone didn't wake me," she said. She crossed the room and sat next to him on the sofa. "Who called?"

"The official Fed doc. Yesterday while you were painting I put a call in to him, leaving a message that I was ready to be checked over. That guy gets up with the chickens, so I knew he'd phone early. Anyway, he'll be here this afternoon."

"Here?"

"It works better that way. Some guys try to push it, report in before they're ready, and if they travel to try to get the medical release it just sets them back even more. It saves the taxpayers' dollars in the long run to have the doctor come to us."

"Oh, well, I guess that makes sense," Kristin said, nodding.

"As soon as I get this medical release we can firm up our plans to be married," he said, taking her hand in his. "And move to Washington. And have a baby. And—"

Kristin laughed delightedly. "Could I settle for a cup of coffee for the moment?"

"Oh, sure thing."

"Thank you, sir," she said, starting toward the kitchen.

"Two babies," Josh called after her. He paused. "Or maybe three. Or maybe even—"

"You're pushing your luck, Quinn!" Kristin yelled back.

Josh hooted with laughter.

Kristin wasn't sure what a doctor who was in charge of the government's secret agents would look like, but she did know that Dr. Nelson did not fit the image she had begun to put together.

The good doctor was short and round and had white hair and a full white beard. Kristin had the irrational thought that she should peek out the window to see if he had arrived in a sleigh with eight reindeer.

Josh made the introductions, and then he and the doctor went down the hall toward the bedroom.

"She's too pretty for an ugly bum like you, Quinn," Kristin heard the doctor say.

"I know that and you know that, but Kristin doesn't know that," Josh said, "so put a cork in it."

The doctor laughed, and so did Kristin as she went into the kitchen to make a fresh pot of coffee and warm a coffee cake.

Half an hour later the pair returned, and Kristin offered them her snack. The three settled onto chairs at the kitchen table.

"I'll turn in your medical release, Quinn," Dr. Nelson said. "You're fit as a fiddle."

"Good," Josh said, nodding.

"Delicious cake, Kristin," Dr. Nelson said. "You're definitely a prize. I understand you're going to marry this reprobate."

"Yes, I am," Kristin said, smiling.

"Tsk, tsk, there's no accounting for taste," Dr. Nelson said. "No, seriously, I'm happy for you both. I'm glad you'll be teaching the green agents, Quinn. You'll make my job a little easier if they learn some of what you know. You're the finest there is. I've patched you up a few times over the years, but nothing compared to some of those other yo-yos they have out in the field. When are you moving to Washington?"

"I'm not sure," Josh said, reaching for another piece of coffee cake. "We didn't want to make definite plans until I got a release from you. I have vacation time coming. I'd like to take Kristin on a honeymoon."

"Oh, how nice," Kristin said.

"Well," Dr. Nelson said, "you deserve some compensation for marrying this dud, Kristin."

"Here he goes again," Josh said, chuckling. He lighted a cigarette with the gold lighter.

"That's bad for your health," Dr. Nelson said.

"So is being an agent." Josh grinned.

"You've got a point there," the doctor said, nodding. He chuckled. "Now, Chet Bell is hazardous to his health just getting up in the morning."

"Chet?" Kristin said. "I know him. He's a very nice young man. Has something happened to him?"

"Oh, no, he's fine," Dr. Nelson said, laughing. "He's being razzed from here to Sunday, but he's being a good sport about it. Seems he decided to try fly-fishing on his vacation, having never fished before in his life. The dumb kid whipped that pole back and—zing—the hook snagged him right in the—" he glanced quickly at Kristin "—the sit-me-down."

"Oh, dear," Kristin said.

Josh laughed.

"Well," the doctor went on, "that thing was really in there for good, and in a place where Chet just couldn't reach it. So he hobbled all the way up to the road and flagged down a trucker. The driver was laughing so hard he could hardly get the blasted thing out."

"Is Chet really all right?" Kristin said.

"Except for still being teased to death, he's as good as new. He couldn't sit down real well for a bit. He's healed up fine, though. It happened a while back. He went on vacation around the same time you were wrapping you and Koltsov around that tree in that car, Quinn.''

Uh-oh, Josh thought. Ah, damn.

"What?" Kristin said. "Chet went on vacation when?"

"Let's see," Dr. Nelson said, stroking his chin. "He signed out . . . Yes, I saw his file. He brought you to Washington, Kristin, then went on vacation the next day. He would have been safer staying on duty."

"The next day," Kristin repeated, looking at Josh.

Josh was studying the end of his cigarette as though he'd never seen such a fascinating thing before in his life.

"Well, I'm off," Dr. Nelson said, getting to his feet. "Thank you for the coffee and cake, and every happiness to you both. I'm sure I'll see you in Washington."

"That would be lovely," Kristin said as the three of them walked to the door.

Dr. Nelson left with a cheerful wave. Kristin returned the wave, then closed the door and slowly turned to look at Josh. He was standing by the fire, his hands in his back pockets. Kristin leaned against the door and crossed her arms over her breasts.

"That's interesting," she said.

"What is?" Josh asked, all innocence.

"Why would someone who is on vacation take me on an extended tour of Washington, come back here with us, then receive a call saying he was needed on an important assignment? According to Dr. Nelson, Chet had checked out at that point. Don't you find that interesting, Josh?"

He squinted at her, trying to find a clue to what she was thinking. She had a rather bland expression on her face, he realized, and was speaking in a pleasant tone of voice. Ah, damn it, he was a dead man. He had only one choice—tell her the truth.

"Oh, man," he said, throwing up his hands. "Kristin, I swear to you, I totally forgot about Chet's harebrained plan. I was so busy going over every detail of my assignment, making sure I told you everything, explained it all down to the smallest thing, that I just plain forgot."

"Harebrained plan?" she said, her expression still unreadable.

"Fred Jones was in on it, too. Chet put it together after you ran out of my hospital room. He knew I needed some time alone with you so I could try to convince you not to dump me, so he put the wheels in motion and called it—"

"Official procedure," Kristin said, nodding. "Ah, yes, I remember. Then he got a call right after we arrived here, and off he went, on an urgent assignment. Which was, in actuality, a rendezvous with a dangerous fishing pole. Yes, this is definitely very interesting."

Josh crossed the room to stand in front of her. "Kristin, listen, okay? I honestly forgot about it. Now I guess you're thinking I'm going to try to rationalize this, as you put it, by saying it wasn't important enough to mention. Well, I'm not going to do that. It *was* important, because it involved you, and I should have told you and— But, damn it, I forgot!"

"I see."

"Ah, hell, I can't read you at all," he said, dragging a hand through his hair. "You're just standing there as though we're chatting about the weather. I'm asking you to trust me on this, Kristin. Damn it, what are you thinking?"

"I think," she said slowly, "that you and Chet and Fred Jones are..." She stopped speaking, stared up at the ceiling and tapped her fingertip against her chin.

"Here it comes," Josh muttered.

Kristin looked at him again. "...are very sweet, dear, romantic men."

"Huh?"

She smiled. "Oh, Josh, I believe that you forgot to tell me about the plan. I believe you for the simple reason that I trust you. And I love you so very much."

Josh released a rush of air, only then realizing that he'd been holding his breath. "And I love you, Kristin Duquesne. Thank you, my love." A wide smile broke across his face. "The future is ours now. We'll be married, have a honeymoon, then move to Washington and really start our life together. I'll mow the grass, leave my socks on the floor, just like a regular, ordinary husband."

"Joshua Quinn, I refuse to pick up your dirty socks."

"Oh. Well, I thought I was supposed to leave my socks— Don't worry. I'll get the hang of this husband bit. We're going to be fantastic together, Kristin."

"We're going to be...perfect. Yes, perfect. And there will be no more secrets."

He swung her up into his arms. "Not a one." He started across the room.

"I love you, Josh."

"And I love you."

When they entered the bedroom, Josh stopped, Kristin still held tightly in his arms.

"Uh-oh," he said.

"What's wrong?"

"I just remembered that I do have another secret."

"What—what is it?"

He grinned at her. "I hate clam chowder."

"Oh, for Pete's sake," she said, punching him on the arm.

Their mingled laughter danced through the air, then quickly changed to whispered endearments and declarations of love as they became one, uniting their bodies, their hearts...

And their souls.

Souls that had been touched by love.

*   *   *   *   *

Silhouette Special Edition

JANUARY TITLES

SKIN DEEP
Nora Roberts

TENDER IS THE KNIGHT
Jennifer West

SUMMER LIGHT
Jude O'Neill

REMEMBER THE DAFFODILS
Jennifer Mikels

IT MUST BE MAGIC
Maggi Charles

THE EVOLUTION OF ADAM
Pat Warren

Silhouette Desire Romances

YOU'RE INVITED TO ACCEPT
4 SILHOUETTE DESIRE ROMANCES AND A TOTE BAG
FREE!

Acceptance card

How to enter

All the words listed overleaf, below the word puzzle, are hidden in the grid. You can find them by reading the letters forwards, backwards, up or down, or diagonally. When you find a word, circle it, or put a line through it. After you have found all the words the remaining letters (which you can read from left to right, from the top of the puzzle through to the bottom) will spell a secret message.

Don't forget to fill in your name and address in the space provided and pop this page in an envelope (you don't need a stamp) and post it today. Hurry - competition ends 30th June 1989

Only one entry per household please.

Silhouette Competition,
FREEPOST,
P.O.236,
Croydon,
Surrey CR9 9EL

Secret message _____

_____

Name_____

Address_____

_____

_____

_____Postcode_____

SCOMP